THE **TANK** MUSEUM

PANTHER

FIBEL

The translation of this work was undertaken by Katie Thompson of the Tank Museum Archive while gestating her own little masterpiece – Daniel.

First published in 1944.
This edition first published in 2021.

British Library Cataloguing in Publication Data.
A catalogue record for this book is available from the British Library.

ISBN 978 1 9163559 2 7

Designed and produced by JJN Publishing Ltd in collaboration with The Tank Museum.

Published by The Tank Museum 2021.

Printed and bound in the UK.

INTRO

Those with an interest in German tanks of the Second World War – and there are many – have probably heard of the *Tigerfibel*, a small volume intended to give instruction to Tiger crews. It was a radical departure from the standard type of German vehicle manual as it contained jokes, cartoons, rhymes and ditties. Fewer, perhaps, know that it was followed by a volume for the Panther. The *Tigerfibel* has been reproduced a number of times – this volume, as far as we are aware, is the first time the *Pantherfibel* has been reproduced and published in English.

For the information it reveals about the use, maintenance and intended combat activity of probably the most effective German tank of the Second World War, it is a fascinating and revealing document. This is a publication that contains the information that those in authority wanted the crews to be familiar with – not what grabs our fancy as a gamer, modelmaker or enthusiast today. In this it shows how so much time must have been taken in simple maintenance to keep such a complex tank available for action. But it is also an example of the graphic art of the period, a topic of wartime German design less often studied.

The Panther

Considered by many to be the finest tank of the Second World War – the Panther (or Sd.Kfz. 171) was, as all tanks are, a compromise in its balancing of firepower, mobility and protection. It was a remarkable success, especially when considering the limiting factors faced by German designers and industry, but it also reflected some of these limitations. While the Tiger, as a 'breakthrough' tank, had been commissioned before the German invasion of the Soviet Union in June 1941, the Panther was a direct response to the experience of the German military meeting Soviet tanks.

The appearance of the Red Army's KV1 and T-34 tanks facing the German invasion should not have been the shock it was – pictures of the T-34 had been published in open source magazines. However, the sight of their standard 3.7cm anti-tank guns failing to penetrate the frontal armour of the KV1 and T-34s was a salutary experience for German troops. The new 5cm Pak 38 anti-tank gun was only just starting to appear with frontline German troops. With few radios, poor leadership and largely inexperienced operatives, the larger Soviet tank forces were outwitted by their German opponents in the opening engagements, but the armour of the heavier Soviet tanks and the firepower of their 76mm guns led to a swift reappraisal by

A Panther Ausf. D that was completed by the Daimler-Benz factory in August 1943.

the Germans of their own tank programme. Designers and manufacturers were sent to the front to see captured examples of the vehicles, which led to a realisation that the medium tanks then in German service were not well armed or armoured enough, and those being designed as replacements were not up to the job. The question was asked if the simple copying of a captured example of a T-34 by German industry was possible. Industry came back with the quite sensible response that by the time the vehicle emerged, Soviet design would have moved on. There was also the consideration that a straight copy simply would not be possible in Germany owing to the ongoing shortages of key alloys. The lack of certain raw materials was a continuing problem for German industry throughout the war. Alloys to assist in the production of armour plate and the limited supplies of aluminium (for which the Luftwaffe had the priority demand) meant an aluminium engine block, as used in the T-34, would not be possible.

A competition was therefore initiated, such was the standard practise in German military vehicle procurement, but with an added urgency. The design specifications for the new medium tank (given the design code VK3002) listed all-round sloped armour (60mm on the front and 40mm on the sides), a maximum weight of 35 tons and a road speed of 55kmh (35mph). The specifications were given to Daimler-Benz and Maschinenfabrik Augsburg-Nürnberg (MAN). In an amazingly short space of time designs were submitted – and the Daimler-Benz model was radical in design with its proposal of a diesel engine.

This captured Hitler's interest – but the German military argued for the more traditional MAN design, which was accepted for development in May 1942.

MAN wins the contract

The MAN treatment featured the standard German tank layout, with 16 sets of interleaved roadwheels and a double torsion bar suspension system. This system, although complex, would give the Panther an outstandingly smooth ride. The MAN design would use the Maybach V12 HL 230P30 petrol engine, a compact design that was also being used in the Tiger I tank. Both the MAN and Mercedes-Benz designs would have been fitted with a new gun designed by Rheinmetall-Borsig – the 7.5cm KwK 42 L/70 gun. This high-velocity gun firing Pzgr.39/42 armour piercing projectiles could penetrate 120mm of armour at 1,000m. The MAN design incorporated a turret already developed by Rheinmetall, which was one of the key factors in MAN winning the contract. The Daimler-Benz design would need a new turret and that would take further development time.

The increasing weight of the new vehicle meant that the traditional steering brake system to allow the vehicle to turn would not be feasible. The new regenerative epicyclic steering system that was being produced for the Tiger tank seemed a suitable answer, but a lack of adequate machine tools meant not enough of the planetary ring gears could be cut – the Panther was intended to be built in much larger numbers than the Tiger. MAN, therefore, had to create a new steering system with spur reduction gears and, while these did work, they were under greater stress than the Tiger system and were prone to more failures. Lack of alloys meant the gears had to be heat treated to help harden them. They also needed a driver who was confident and smooth in his gear-changing, something that needed training time – a feature that was lacking for tank crews as the war progressed.

Hitler insisted on the increase in armour from 60mm to 80mm on the front glacis plate of the tank – even though hulls with 60mm had already started to be assembled. Testing of components took place in the autumn of

1942 and inevitably changes were made to the design that went into series production. For example, the turret had a bulge to accommodate the commander's offset cupola that was quickly eliminated to simplify production. Cracks in gears still proved a problem, but production tanks were required for Hitler's proposed spring offensive in 1943. The number of failures meant rebuild programmes had to take place, delaying issue to frontline units.

The offensive at Kursk – Operation Citadel – was postponed by Hitler until July to allow more Panthers to be completed and used in the operation. Preparation for the offensive had been long and Soviet defences were well prepared. At the end of the first day's fighting, crews – many lacking in training time – had only 40 of the 192 Panthers available to them still in operation. Subsequent analysis found that tanks were abandoned or destroyed by their crews due to mechanical breakdowns and the lack of suitable recovery vehicles. However, the gun on the tank had proved outstanding.

Rectifying the numerous issues that caused the failures on the early Panthers would usually have occurred during a testing and evaluation programme. German wartime tanks did not have this luxury – but improvements in reliability did occur so that the Panther became statistically as available as the other tanks in German service.

Confusingly, the first production vehicles were Ausführung D (or Model D), not A as might be expected. No B, C or E models were envisaged but Ausführung A (a new turret design) and G (new hull with Ausführung A turret) models followed the D. About 6,000 Panthers were built by the war's end, many showing the modifications that occurred during the production runs when items were simplified, or interruptions occurred due to component supplies or factory stoppages because of the Allied bombing campaign.

The Panther had a superb gun, good frontal armour (but weaker and more vulnerable side armour), and a good level of mobility with its high power-to-weight ratio and wide tracks. It also had good crew ergonomics, communications and sighting systems along with a fair range (150km on the road, 100km cross-country) and a main armament ammunition load of 79 rounds. It was a heavy tank at 44 tons and relatively tall, but at 176,000 Reichmarks only marginally more expensive than the Panzer IV at 117,000 Reichmarks – the Tiger 1 cost 250,000 Reichmarks.

Issue

The tank was first issued to two units, Panzer-Abteilung 51 and 52 in early 1943. Each unit was to have a headquarters company consisting of three tanks in a signal platoon and five tanks in a reconnaissance platoon. There would be four companies of tanks each made up of 22 tanks (a company headquarters of two tanks and four platoons of five tanks). The issuing of tanks to units was dependent on production, and as already mentioned this was interrupted by delays in the manufacture of parts and with distribution issues, as the transport infrastructure became degraded by the bombing of the main factories. Few units ever had a full complement of vehicles as intended, and in the last six months of the war improvised battlegroups saw the Panther being used in ad hoc formations. The Panther saw most service on the Eastern Front and at its height 740 tanks were available with 500 operational, while others would be in transit or undergoing repair etc. It also fought in Italy and on the Western Front, some 471 being present at the end of 1944, with 336 available operationally.

The crew

The tank is often looked at as a sum of its technical parts, but of course all the design and production of the technology is useless without a crew. The German military tried to ensure the training of crews continued to a high standard as the war progressed, however personal accounts reveal how little training some crews actually received. The lack of training and the ability to use the equipment to its full potential was an undoubted reason why Panthers were lost in combat. In September 1944 an American unit with Sherman tanks trounced a Panther unit that, on paper, should have been the more powerful force – simply because the American crews were experienced and the Panther crews lacked training and combat savvy. The need for a Panther driver to be confident and smooth in gear-changing has already been mentioned. The constant need for maintenance and servicing of the vehicle was one of the reasons the *Pantherfibel* was issued. Cards showing grease points, fluid level check points and wear rates were issued and tatty, well-used copies exist in the archive of The Tank Museum, taken no doubt from prisoners-of-war or abandoned vehicles.

The crew positions

The intimacy of the tank space meant that traditional separation of ranks was less apparent in armoured units. The skills of all the crew members were essential for the successful operation of the vehicle, so the building of a trusted team was important to each crew member. They had to depend on each other to have any chance of survival. The roles in a Panther were typical of all German five-man tank crews.

Panther Ausf. D fresh from the factory. The highest monthly number of new tanks accepted by the military was 380 in July 1944.

Kommandant (Commander)

Usually a Feldwebel (staff sergeant) or higher in rank, the commander did just that, commanded the tank in all its use. The commander, with the highest position in the vehicle, had to keep a constant eye on the landscape ahead and transfer any relevant information to the driver. The need to keep a

The German military made great efforts to continue full training courses for tank crews as the war progressed, but inevitably standards dropped and courses were interrupted. The success of the Panther in action depended – as all tanks do – on the skills and motivation of the crew.

sense of what was going on around the vehicle – spatial awareness – meant the commander kept his head out of the turret for as long as possible. Locating minefields, tank traps, enemy anti-tank guns and tanks meant constantly scanning the battlefield. He would also pass targets on to the gunner. A closed-down tank had very limited visibility and in action smoke and fumes added to the problem. The commander also kept vehicle maintenance records and tasked the other crewmembers.

Ladeschütze (Loader)
The loader had the most physically active role in combat, the rate of fire of the tank being dictated by his ability to load the ammunition. Armour Piercing (AP) rounds weighed 21 kg each. Some 79 rounds were carried in the Ausf. D and A, 82 rounds in the Ausf. G, all stowed below the turret in the hull of the vehicle. There was usually a 50/50 split between AP and High Explosive (HE). The loader also had to dispose of empty shell cases when the opportunity arose.

Funker (Wireless Operator)
The Panther was fitted with a FuG 5 radio that had a range of 4-6km. Those tanks issued to headquarters units or platoon leaders were also provided with a FuG 2 shortwave receiver. The wireless operator looked after the radio kit, monitored messages and also operated the bow machine gun, if fitted. Keeping abreast of radio codes, passwords and map references was also the wireless operator's responsibility. The role had a number of general tasks and in many tanks the wireless operator became the cook and general help.

Richtschütze (Gunner)
The gunner was frequently a sergeant and often had more training than other crewmembers. He would take over the tank in the event of the commander's absence or incapacitation. The gunner sat ahead of the commander with limited vision and an exit route through the commander's hatch.

Fahrer (Driver)
The driver had to be able to read the landscape to ensure his tank was best positioned in combat and did not present weaker areas to the enemy. Driving was tiring and stressful so on halts the rest of the crew tried to allow the driver a chance to relax, sleep and recuperate. A sleepy or inattentive driver could prove disastrous for a vehicle.

The *Pantherfibel* as a piece of wartime design.
The Nazis' use of distinctive design created a very recognisable product – a strong 'brand' as it would be known today. The undoubted appeal of the brand at the time and the strong reaction to the Swastika even now, shows something of its power. Interest in military history and militaria means some areas of Nazi branding or design are well known and widely studied – uniforms and insignia for example. However, apart from propaganda posters, graphic design, fine art and film are less well known to a general audience. The *Pantherfibel* is a part of the graphic design of the period and, along with the *Tigerfibel,* it is often referred to as a radical departure in German vehicle manuals and training material – but why so ?

Hitler had a great interest in the effectiveness of design to convey the message he wanted for the Nazi Party. He wrote about the issue in *Mein Kampf*, his rambling political manifesto, and said how he admired Peter Behrens who had designed a corporate identity for the German electrical giant Allgemeine Elektricitäts-Gesellschaft (AEG). Behrens had not only designed a corporate logo for AEG, he had also created a whole range of packaging, advertising and products. Hitler showed a surprising level of interest in the minutiae of how the Party was to be portrayed and he wanted the Party to be present across the spectrum of German life.

While Hitler wanted the Party to be new and forward-looking, he also played on German tradition. There were parts of German history, traditional design and symbols that were incorporated in the new iconography, sometimes with a very modern twist. The Reichsadler – or national eagle – was a long established symbol dating back centuries that had come to represent German unification. In 1935, Hitler ordered that a new version of the eagle, holding a swastika, should become the new national emblem (the Hoheitszeichen).

Parts of the Modernist movement, like the Bauhaus art school, were openly attacked or banned by Hitler – often because of Jewish or left-leaning associations. However, other parts of modern design were used to promote the forward-looking image the Nazis wanted to create. Ironically, the new Autobahn or motorway system had bridges designed by ex-Bauhaus students.

Typography

The competing desires for tradition (Volkism) and to look to the future led to a heated debate within the Party over – of all things – typefaces. When Hitler came to power in 1933 the belief of a number of influential Party members was that Hitler would naturally prefer the 'old', traditional, style of German typeface – heavy, spikey and Gothic, called blackletter. This harking back to a perceived 'Germanic' style led Alfred Rosenberg, the head of a number of Nazi cultural organisations, to mount a campaign between 1933 and 1935 to use only 'deutsche Schrift', or German lettering, instead of any modern or 'degenerate' typestyles. In 1935 Hitler surprised the Volkism supporters by declaring 'petrified backward lookers' were 'dangers to National Socialism'. This led to a number of new typefaces being promoted including very modern-looking sans serif fonts such as Futura.

Blacklettering was still used in official publications, but it was often toned down or used in conjunction with more modern typefaces. Hitler stated that 'To be German means to be clear!', and undoubtedly the legibility of the modern typefaces was better. This, of course, was important in promoting the Nazi message and also in creating a modern-looking image abroad. It, too, was important in official publications such as military training and vehicle maintenance manuals where clarity to the reader and legibility were essential.

The clarity of the newer typefaces over the earlier black Gothic types can be seen in the German training manuals and documents in The Tank Museum archive. The D series of manuals or Dienstvorschriften (service manuals) were issued to cover all aspects of vehicle activity. Each vehicle or weapon entering service was given a number and each manual associated with the item was issued as a sub-number.

The Panther, for example, was allocated the number D 655. The original D 655/5 is a handbook for the driver, 655/24 is the maintenance plan, D655/31C is the manual for the Maybach HL230P engine – and so the list goes on – there are probably dozens of manuals connected to the Panther.

Manuals considered top secret had a + added after the number and a cover printed in red. Internal vehicle systems, including the main armament, have D 200 or D 2000 numbers, while radio equipment is D 900 or D 9000. The Luftwaffe also produced manuals for ground equipment and these were identified as D (Luft). As new models and upgrades came into service, so manuals had to be updated and supplements issued. A plethora

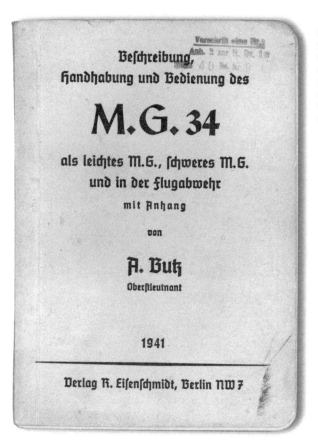

Beschreibung, Handhabung und Bedienung des

M.G. 34

als leichtes M.G., schweres M.G. und in der Flugabwehr

mit Anhang

von

A. Butz
Oberstleutnant

1941

Verlag R. Eisenschmidt, Berlin NW 7

Despite the move towards modern san serif typestyles, the blackface or Gothic lettering was modernised and was still used for manuals – here on a handbook for the MG 34.

The move to the modern clarity of san serif typefaces like Futura can be seen on the cover of this driver's manual for the Panther.

D 655/5

Zum Einlegen in das Gerät!

Pz Kpfw Panther

Ausführung A und D
und Abarten
(Für Ausführung G gilt dieses Handbuch bis zum
Erscheinen der Vorschrift D 655/25)

Handbuch
für den Panzerfahrer

Vom 1. 4. 44

740

of manuals could be associated with a complex vehicle such as a tank.

The use of cartoons featuring young ladies to try and impart information to soldiers was not a new idea for the military. In Britain the artist Roland Penrose used nude images of his wife Lee Miller, camouflaged with body paint, to spice up his lectures to the Home Guard, and in the USA model Chili Williams was used by Army engineers to promote camouflage training. In Germany, cartoons and nudes can be seen in barrack rooms and training environments but not in official training manuals. The introduction of the *Tigerfibel* with cartoons, rhymes and saucy images was therefore a new departure as an official publication, if not that radical as a concept.

The *Tigerfibel* (D656/27) is credited to Lt Joseph von Glatter-Götz, who was tasked with coming up with a training manual by Oberstleutnant Hans Christian, the officer in charge of tank crew training. Glatter-Götz then wrote what he called the *Tiger Primer* with the aim that the information it contained would be interesting, eye-catching and allow the troops to learn quickly. He also used soldiers' jargon, not classroom or formal German. German is a rigid language in terms of register: there are many different 'levels' – from the very formal down to the kind of language used at home with friends and family. Normal German manuals tend to be of a high register using very technical German with a technical vocabulary and construction. This language would be deemed 'appropriate' for the setting, but is not particularly memorable or readable, unlike the poetry and the more chatty style of instructions in the *Tiger* and later *Pantherfibel*. For the *Tigerfibel*, two-tone illustrations were drawn by Obergefreiter Gessinger and Unteroffizier Wagner. The publication was printed by Eisner-Verlag in Berlin and first issued in the autumn of 1943, and for the troops it was 'a complete success'. The official approval for the publication came from Guderian himself.

Pantherfibel style

The authors of the *Pantherfibel* are not, as yet, known, but the publication has differences to the *Tigerfibel*. While it has a similar size, structure, a mix of typefaces and of course the use of rhymes, mottos and ditties along with the cartoon illustrations, in terms of its density, the many classical allusions and fewer saucy illustrations, it does show changes. There are references to real people such as Manfred von Brauchitsch and Rudolf Caracciola, two of the racing drivers from the successful pre-war Mercedes-Benz racing team the Silver Arrows, along with nicknames for characters like Slow Coach, Clever Clogs and Gearstick.

More effort (and perhaps time) has gone into the *Patherfibel* and it seems to show an expectation of a high level of education by those reading it. There are quotes by Voltaire, references to the Laocoön, even a quote from J.F.C. Fuller. Whether the writers thought the soldiers did understand and were familiar with these references is hard to say – or were they trying to show off their own knowledge to superiors? While the references might be educated, the language is more informal when compared to the dry language of the usual technical or official publication.

Amongst the ditties and rhymes there is a lack of overtly political material, but for a modern audience the eye is taken by the almost casual anti-semitic reference to the tailor's shop and by the lumpen Russian soldier with his racially inferior demeanour. Whether soldiers even noticed such references is now hard to judge.

The idea behind the *Tiger* and *Pantherfibel* continues to this day. There are cartoon illustrated manuals and information magazines for the military, and there is even an equivalent for the Leopard tank. The *Pantherfibel* gives us a wealth of information on the practical side of running a Panther in wartime and the expectations of the crew. We have the luxury of reading the booklet now in circumstances very different to those of the original readers. Whatever the jokes, for the men who fought in the Panther – and those who battled against it – this was not a fun time. Let us be thankful we don't have to do the same.

David Willey
March 2021

THANKS TO

The Tank Museum wishes to thank and acknowledge the following who kindly supported the crowdfunding campaign, which enabled this title to be republished in mid-2021.

Steven Malley	Steve Taylor	Matthew E. Carn	Russell Valentine	Max Dahlberg
Samuel Weston	David Jordan	Ian Loader	Robert Dickinson	Steve Williams
Michael Krueger	David Philip Silvester	Luka Jankovic	Tyler Patton	Kelvin Bampfield
Martin C. McCleary	Edward Stott	William Veitch	Kenneth Alexander	Timmy Pugliese
Joel Deluca	Dave Cooper	Peter Green	Peter T. Robinson	Keith Meachem
Tom Flaherty	Jeroen Van Dijk	Alexander Petford	Luke Johns	Sean O'Hara
Michael Moore	Alek Eligh	Andrew 'Bob' Whitworth	David Makinson	Ron Ashker
Pete Christopher James	Adam Lavender	Mark Knight	Fergal Ramsay	Graeme Flint
Christopher Godfrey	Des Parrott	Stephen Watton	Kasey Thompson	Simon Dean
Rob Kramer	Alan Wilson	John Cook	Adrian Mansfield	Billy Digiulio
Alex Roberts	Michael Christie	Jordan Weaver	Sébastien Vinel	Dave Batten
Dave Basford	John Blunden	Chuck Bell	Norman Cooke	Robert Prosperi
Sebastian Palmer	Michael Gallasch	Eddie Jackson	Alex Trenchard	George McEwan
Arron Chiswell	Paul Hachey	James White	Glyn Davies	Jan Lambrecht
Guy Silberrad	Walter Perdue	Neil Allen	Kris Lockyear	James Daniels
Paul Mutton	Albert McNamara	Cheston Cunha	Kevin Brown	Michael Woong
Simon Norburn	Adam Fanthorpe	John Edward Dickinson	Alexander W. Lee	Robert Wildish
Simon Batchelor	Tim Maese	Chris Wood	Ian Worrall	Oliver Watts

Nathaniel Goodwin
Peter Thomas
John Heath
Alan Mincher
Peter Smith
Yousuf Hamza Brookhouse
Peter Edwards
Mark Price
Thomas Grindall
Kenneth Leslie Gorman
Marcus Riganelli
Ferdinand Hubmann
Nick Cross
Callum Debloois
Michael Patey
Steve Rothwell
George E. Atkinson
Chris Clark
Bollaert Jean-Michel
Michael Miller
Lefebvre Mathieu
Rod Sayers
Frank Van Hooft
Wayne Barnard
James Buckley
4th/7th RDG

Iestyn King
Ian Tooley
Charles Winkley
Barry Thackray
Pete Lawrence
Stewart Garnett
Thomas Bell
Cathy Tooley
Brian Loughran
Marco Schraver
Deverne Jones
J.W. Frolick
Lyn Richardson
Kevin Reardon
Richard Arnesen
Martin Agar
4th/7th RDG
Martin Jones
Brian Tombaugh
Matt Klotz
Jake Elstob
Kevin Clark
Sam Barratt
Stephen Keeler
Steve Durrant
Peter Hall

Nick Callaghan
Richard Duval
Oli Mattholie
Kirk Ashley-Morgan
Pete Clarke
John Whitehouse
David Shanks
Barry John
Rossa
Scott Davenport
Hugh Murden
Damon Cochrane
David Donohue
Richard Carter
Lee Powell
Steve MacSorley
George Appleby
Thomas Corneill
Peter Allman
Ismael Amor Garcia
De San Teodoro
James Ballantyne
Patrick Katalenas
Danny Hin
Tony Steele
Alexander James Leighton

Richard Charlton-Taylor
Chris Jack
Neil Beasant
Talana Gamah
Aiden Terris
Nick Vujcich
Derek Wisdom
Mark Hughes
Caleb Lester
Matthijs Dijkgraaf
James Mitchell
Jan Bergholtz
Steve Gregory
Nelson Jackson
Mikael Rydfalk
Ian Wilcox
Eamonn Melaniphy
Jacob Roberts
Steve Bastable
Martin Hart
Graham Rhodes
Maurício Conceição
Wayne Birks
Bobby Derbyshire
Guy Meisl
Trevor Wilson

Nigel Bruce
Toby Isherwood
Rupert Pritchard
Richard W Barnes
Sheridan Falkenberry
Liam Heaney
Glyn Williams
Jack Crosby
Martin Short
Richard Burton
Daniel Green
Richard Brown
Michael Xenikakis
Ananiadis
Mathew Clark
Stephen Reid
Paddy Kelly
John Reardon
David Cruickshank
Michael Greenhorn
Bob Carr
Dallas Hayes
Hans-Peter Quambusch
Robert Simmons
Matias Veijalainen
Paul Garratt

Michael Boyer
Gary Slegg
Bryan Stinton
Mike Tawton
Simon Miller
Robert Sobotka
Simon Longlands
John Foreman
Quentin Challis
Lee Archer
Alex Buckley
David W Innes
Paul Spinner
Kenneth Lilley
Thomas Jack
 Wilts RHG/D
Steve Jury
Philip Gibbs
Stuart Harrison
Mick Green
Timothy A. Torres
Marcin Skrok
Paul A. Dodsworth
Jeroen Vantroyen
Roger Peachey
Nigel Chappell

Bill Gilmour
Duncan Nottage
David Markov
Scott Gill
Andrew F. Smith
Philip Reynolds
Ron Wright
Connar Fyfe
Staley Snook
Andrew Strangeway
Jasper Carlier
Stuart Bainbridge
Paul Fitzpatrick
Terry Hall
Ian Rashbrook
Thijs Lepstra
Mike L'Alouette
Timothy Fitzer
Tom Davies
Bruce Carrington
Caleb Joy
Keith Roberts
Tony Fargher
Andrew Wedge
Trevor Kane
Gil Verthaim

Lee Thompson
Pete Lowen
John Masker
Paul Goffin
Markku Selin
Jason Hayward
Toon Schouteten
Lewis Kraty
Richard Featherstone
Matt Dawson
Matteo Miconi
Stephen Whitehead
Mark Dodd
Johnny Doyle
Alan Whybrow
Leo Van Meerbergen
Alex Capitain
Joshua C.T. Cornell
Dave Berrey
Jonathan De Vecchi
Freeman
Doug Kennedy
Maj William H. Holzer
David S. Marks
Sneaky Git
Michael Williams

Tom Ryan
Euan Griffiths
Murphy Family
Ross Wilson
Nigel Warman
James Birmingham
Francis Peltgen
Michael (Buff) Brown
Stewart Charman
The Battle Barge
Michael Guthrie
Andrew Hillier
Jeremy Bell
Nicholas Morland
Kent Meyers
Janwillem Helleman
Patrick Hughes
Fred Thompson
Andrew Gilbert
Hew McDermott
Steve Wellen
David Crooks
Arran Hartley
Hans Johansson
Ron Hoague
Bram Zantingh

Akira Hasegawa
David Breakwell
Stijn Anthoni
Darren Astles
Graham Hind
Tony Gaynor
Alan Jones
Mike Handford
 ex-17/21L
Frederick S Nissen
Rhys Fouracre
Luke B.
Keith Ewington
Mac McCartney
Rachael Sullivan
Richard Stevens
Tony Vickers
Craig Hawes
Leon Munro
Gareth 'Rommel' Hoole
Dave Howling
Andrew Smurthwaite
James Fox
Herminio Ramirez III
Lucas Salazar
Jamie Foster

Karl Butsch	Paul Emore	John D. Wright	Paul Dubber	Manuel Soriano
Richard Erny	Brent Buszka	Carl Franzon Uvebrant	Johan Van Der Bruggen	Joseph Toole
Hideki Kuniya	Chris Liddiard	Keith Warren	Mark Andrews	Alan Fenwick
Graham Clifton	Trevor Fetherstonhaugh	Frank Burge	Bruce Vautier	Mike Corser
Dwight Luetscher	William R. Dixon	Nick Vaughan	Richard Groundsell	Wannes Van Causbroeck
Quentin Ford	Jacob Katt	Nicholas Griffin	Jason Boswell	Richard Gill
Lee A'Court	David Macklin	David Hutchby	John A Smith	Alexander Nelmes
Michael Rayner	Geoff McConville	Johan Brandhammar	Angus J. Thorne	Kevin Pierce
Kieran O'Connor	Steven 'Tommy' Lawton	Kees Lit	David P.H. Molloy	Jack Nash
Kevin Tompkins	Roger Stakkestad	Benjamin Craze	Derek Armstrong	Paul Spandler
Lewis McCoy	Mark Preston	Warren Fenner	Stephen Booth	Reinhardt Derlich
Andy Rolfe	Lindsay Ellis-Barnes	Max Jones	Jonathan Nielsen-Moore	Cameron Maxwell
Julian Ginniver	Alistair McRae	William Calvert	Derek Marshall	Ashley Smyth
Reid Vizcarra	Simon Thompson	Karl Scott	Alexander Gibson	Michael Brookes
Mikkel Petrich	Robert F. Riemer	Sandy Eisen	Bod Weller	Chris Brinkman
Aaron Hollander	John Sullivan	Thomas Weekes	Eric Reifsteck	Jon Ander Merino
Lowell Wong	Shaun Poller	Michael Weekes	Callum Murray	Alastair Boyles
Alex H.	Robin McEwen	Mike Grattidge	Paul Adamson	Hasan Mussa
Ron Merkel	Florian Kuelb	Dean Salvador	Robert L. Loonstyn	Martin Wilby
David Lomas	Overwatch	Graham Green	Quentin Wright	Freddie Fowler
Mark Evans	Peter Scott-Samuel	Richard J. Tugwell	Chris Jenkins	Julien Dessimoz
Rob Murray	D. Johnston	Ryan Van Hien	Lee Smith	Oliver William Tucker
Greg Fysh	Mika Doody	Catalin Oprea	Jonathan Hedley Barnes	Christopher Ferguson MD
Toby Teague	Stuart Purvis	Sam Rickman	Bob Price	Michael Schwartz
SGM Jim Peterson	Ozmundo	Mark Cuttle	Peter Fox	Alejandro Pascual
Jack Green	J. Josef Rozzell PhD	Samuel Whyman	Clive Constable	Paul Franklin

James Stutheit
Gary Dhillon
Zebulon Swinney
Anders Persson
Barry Hill
Gavin S. Kay
Paul Biro
David Lomas
Jaime Saunders
Gary Relihan
Jason Passfield
Tom Mosher Jr
Gary Sullivan
Don Beary
Lauren Child
Tom Mercer
Leasa Aldous
William Pointer
Steven Blackburn
Gary Sullivan
James Futers
Mark Towner
David Corboy
Master Dollard
Alfie Mullett
Oscar Martin

Bruce Worrall
Shaun Parry
Chris Burberry
Duncan Connell
Dirk Bonnez
Anders Hekland
Joshua Bettinelli
Jack Speight
Steve Wren
Alan & Heather Pardon
Stephen Hendrie
Karl Fey
Damian Van Velzen
Michael Earnshaw
Duncan Townend
Nick Collingridge
Perry Kitson
David Roche
Mark Roche
Douglas Gleeson
Hubert Danielsson
Stephen Rodger Benson
Timothy C. Wright
Jason Morrison
Joe Powell
Steven Ecott

Richard Baxter
Ian Noble
Michael Denoon-Slater
Colin A. Rixon
Bobh
Michael Boswell
John St John
Mark Gruener
Gordon & Kathi Baker
Eddie Ward
Kirk Shelley MD PhD
David Preece
Sjouke Attema
Mark Hawkes
Yeoman Warder Shady Lane
Henry Jasper Arrowsmith
Jonathan Cruickshank
Gary Watson
Martin Littlecott
Matthew Gunning
Dominic Quinn
Tom Hardy
Frank Waite
Logan Metesh
Michael Salata
Tim Read

Jefferson Bledsoe
Scott Weed
John Conran
Davey Boer
Louis Turner
Andy Watson
Mark Randall
John Chance
Scott Fitzgerald
Fredrik 'Panzerranger'
   Karlsson
Devlin James Roderick
Charlie Newman
Aiden Reichl
Saul Smith
Ronald Pietjouw
John Stanbridge
Mark Jeffery
Paul Howson
Phil Newell
Thomas Barnes
Richard Florance
Keith McDonald
Peter Chidgey-Hallan
Brian Siela
Brian Jones

Iori Hicks
Wolfram
Oliver Wilson
Michael Worrell
Paul Cocks
Domenic Liggett
Michael Trucchi
Daryl Gamble
Graham Wedlock
Jack Robling
Richard Thompson
Boot Weasel
H. Mowbray
Peter J. Stewart.
Paul Bowden
Lleyton Kuypers
Tom Somers
Keith Pattison
Robert Davies
Mark Bisley
Mike Tice
Gary Richardson
Brennan Ferrington
Justin De Lavison
Richard Thompson
Alex Fouts

Shengxuan Cui	Regan Robinson	Anthony Shortland	Colin Belbin	Marcus Davys
Mark William Niblett	Eric O. Costello	Edward Hooper	John Sigsworth	Sjoerd Wiersma
William Caton	Trevor Ford	Raymond Wong	David Abbott	Jarvin Amacna
James Dunsheath	Scott Meyer	Raymond Wong	Martin Deacon	James Carver
Jim Botts	Andrew Devenport	Joseph F. Budde	Mark Wayne Holm	Khem Aikwanich
Vincent Senne Willems	Marc Hope	David William Davies	Elliot Wade	Jason Bell
Charles Paterson	Nick Meredith	Jonathon Ratsey	Chris Stickney	Graham Dunbar Brown
David Vokes	Jake Vaughan	Saraj Guha	Flynn Wesley	Joseph Sproston
Mark Tassinari	Kurt Bullington	Sandy Auston	Richard Wartnaby	Ethan Schmeelk
Aaron McCormick	United States Army	Graham Wood	Colin Howley	Patrick Doyle
Frank Østergaard	Brotherhood of Tankers	Steve Ellis 5 Innis DG	Matthew Riches	Tim Polman
James V Carr	Michael Stanley	Cameron Graham	Robin Payne	Paul Flanary
Dave Sharman	Stephen Kawamura	Alastair McMurray	Adrian Symonds	James Watts
Jorrit Kelder	Chris Saunders	Brian Gunter	Paul Softley	Mark Hanson
David Buchanan	Jeremy Youmans	James Steele	Sarah Skates	Steve Humphrey
Sean Tighe	Jim Fall	Chris Elyea	Ryan Morgan	Grahame Andrew
Ka Ki Leung	Victor Muñoz	Adam Yeates	Aaron	Simon Kennerley
Anthony Grayson	Jack Maher	Simon Clayton	Chris Blackler	Joe Chesters
Scott Lockhart	David G Brown	Steve Clark	Vebjørn Nergård	Michal Koos
Adrian Mace	Joe Lewis	Uwe Stolz	Mike Brothwell	Richard Booth
Craig McGhee	David Ogilvie	Keir Coford	Andrew Thompson	Lisa Hutson
Chris Smith	Neil Stokes	John Fenton	Paul Fuller	James Armstrong
Skyler Waker	David Walker	Sicco Miedema	Matthew Capper	Darren Middleton
David Lewis	Javier Tapia	Robert Colson	Reme Greenie	Alan Johnson
Collin Short	Tyrone Karl Mullin	Andrew James	Matt Wells	Travis Yelland
Vincent Miller	Anthony D. Morley	Shaun Richards	Ian Davies	Martyn-Ellis Ward

J.J. McLeod
Blake Johnson
Colin Pearce
Anders Tyrén
Matthew Onion
David Morris
Simon Smith
Dave Storey
Antony Baldwin
Michael Farlam
George Bramwell
Emmett Gribben
Richard Perry
Tom Hay
Mark Hamilton
Crazy Mad Boris
Roland Vdb
Melvin Mast
John Andersen
Leonard Leach
Ryan Allen
Zachary Paterson
Elliot Moore
Martin Tuck
Brian A. Sanders
Matthew Nutt

Philip D. Middleton
David Hathaway
Andrew Kenny
Tony Carbuto
Nicholas Cobbold
Christopher Shields
Gary O'Rourke
Zeke Wallace-Wells
Jordan Lawrie
Michael Richter
Leon Moberg
Jack Ellison
Michael Hendrik
Metcraft-Beath
Mark Currier
David Lewin
Michael Cooper
Tom Grossman
Ford Fitch
Jimmy Zhan
Mark A. Burroughs
Ian Mittell
Adam Reynolds
Aaron L. Earle
Tom Kistruck
Mircea Preda

John Barry
James Neesom
Terry Read
Jon Dillon
David Pyle
Billy Austin
Jordan Whitbread
Carl Doran
Goran Lowkrantz
Paul Cook
Bob Norris
Owen Haggerty
Chris Collins
Christopher Randall
Glen Hawkins
Alek/Konrad Bogacki
Dominic Miele
Zeb Doyle
Steve Shields
Henry Teague
Nathan Parker
Walter W. Keller II
Matt Hill
Stephen Cairns
Charlie Trumpess
Dickon Barry

Andrew Smith
Bernie Mark
Kevin Quine.
Oscar Smith
Ieuan Buckley
Jack Taylor
J.M.G.M.
Dougie Smith
Michael Robins
Josh Lockett
Colin MacKenzie
Charlie Stevens
Jonathan Russell
S. McLuckie
Georg Eyerman
Nick Jones
Jared L. Vernon
Joshua Pinchbeck
Palladion Hearts
Matthew Gettings
Stuart Hully
Adam Hall
Chris Ribbons
Charles Toler
Phelepos Zoukas
Darren Waters

Niels Jansen
Graeme Bates
Jarred Klein
Gary Neilson
Alex
Hailey Ng
Thomas Charles Tye
Logan
Jackson Snodgress
Ian Kuhlman
Kevin Akins
Ryan Morgan
Richard Griffiths
Jacob Tierney
Simon Clark
Thomas Lindon
James Wilkinson
Michael Grimwood
Andrew Mansfield
Gary Elmes
Ralph Barker
Rutger Smeenk
Martin Leckonby
Craig Henderson
Jonathan Newland
Jo Silverthorn

Alex Robinson
Edgar Bissell
Robert L. Cogan
Ryan Davis
John Drummey
William Barrett
John Deeley
Joseph Morgan
Adrian Lucas
Tyler Keely
Nels Bruckner
Gabe Schmit
N. Natsu
James Graham Bell
Tom Noble
Colin Gibson
Darion Owen Carlisle
Alexander Pebbie
Piet Van Grinsven
Simon Hutchinson
Pedro Jonas
Jonah Rice
Shaun Bojko
Mark Classen
Tommy McDaniel
John Marsden

Colin Graham
Peter Bowyer-Frost
Joshua Olwell
Christopher Ludena
Mitch Hamilton
Thomas R Wetherall
Kieran Messer
Matthew Nobbs
David Graham Ord
Eli Danby
Tom Close
Roger Hall
Sten Henriksson
Alexander Morgan Jones
Martin Reithmayr
Raj Mehta
Thomas Hu
Capt A.E. Knuth
   USN (Ret)
Nigel Frampton
Philippe Andre
Peter Mackle
Matthew Spreadbury
Joseph Wolfenden-
Williams
Derrick Johnson

David Winter
Kevin Bradley
Sibout Pauwels
James Wilson Oram
Lewis Martin
Sander B. Berge
Ryley Fry
Paul Eddington
Jonathan Purser
Anthony Wishart
Peter Ward
Michael David Groves
Brendon Read
Kai Allen
Alex Carr
Ben Ward
Olly Bevan
Richmond Lam
Geoffrey Stobbart
Richard Rolfe
Connor Cooper
Michael Dickson
Mark Dewfall
James L. Boyle
Colin Hume
Arved Aasmaa

Julian Charlesworth
Connor Craig
Owen Preston
Geoffrey Stevens
Richard Ferguson
Joshua Bell
Dylan Milne
Haytham Gardee
Will Bleyer
Tom Bishop
Gavin MacGregor
Darren Line
Brian Wills
Brian Nicklas
Aaron Hutson
Zach Powell
Nick Massaro
Joseph C. Oppenheim
Ron Schroer
Cameron Baxter
Neil Johnson
Adrian Lidington
Simon George
Kevan & Sam Downey
Thomas Phillipart
Austin Hindley

Benedict Rowe
Ryoji Sakai
Dean Borg
Joe Sherman
Charles Gouldmann
David Chadwick
Morten Klintø Hansen
Nathaniel Wardroper
Hughes
Paul Watson
Michael Devereux
Jonathan Hammond
Nathan Stephenson
Adam Sadecki
Vincent Castellani
Rune Gustafsson
Andrew Mottram
Richard Cooper
Daniel House
Łukasz Janowski
Pieter Bart Van Kekem
Andrew Abernethy.

Alles zu sagen, ist das Geheimnis [1]
langweilig zu sein.   Voltaire

1. To say everything is the secret to being boring.

2. To be respectable is like a jewel
But it'll serve you here as good as gruel.
Through knowledge and fun and varied too,
It'll seem half as difficult for you.
Mixed in with a few scintillations
And some aide memoire foundations,
And while this Panther punch is enriching,
Everyone, dead easy, is building (not botching).
Berlin, 1944

You don't know anything, let's be clear,
So this command's vital, do you hear?
Your shock at this we can curtail,
Mix up a Panther boozy cocktail.

The Panther crewman's three sheets, looks
Like an army issue tank guidebook.
But your very own innate cleverness
He achieves naturally in his tipsiness.
He floats above the mountains
Surrounded by cartridge mountings.
When he wakes from this excitement,
In his sleep he's been enlightened,
With what one needs to know exactly.

Parole:

Lerne mit Genuß!

1. Panther Punch, 2. Tip: Learn with fun and jocularity!

CONTENTS

B O O K S ,   S H E E T S ,   D R A W I N G S ,   T R A I N I N G

Books		Page number	Erlangen 1	
			General	
D 655/1	Company Technical Description and Operating Instructions for the Chassis	1	Plan for Re-training	
D 655/1a	Cross Sectional Drawings of the Gearbox and Steering	2	Structure of a Panther Detachment	
D 655/2	Technical Description and Operating Instructions for the Turret	3 5—7	Technical Data for Armoured Vehicles and Weapons / What do you need to know about Anti-Gas Defence?	
D 655/4b	Logbook for Lubrication and Maintenance	1	Technical Information for Armoured Vehicles / Regenerative Steering	
D 655/5	Handbook for the Tank Driver	2	Automatic Fire Extinguishing System	
D 655/27	Panther Primer	3	Electrical Installation Considerations for the Armoured Vehicle Mechanic	
D 655/30 a — c	Repair Instructions for the Armoured Vehicle Mechanic	4	For the Attention of the Panther Driver!	
D 655/31a—c	Workshop Handbook	5	Lubricants	
D 655/60	Accompanying Booklet	6	Maintenance of the Liquid Gas System	
D 622/10	Practical Tips for Repair Service	7	Tank Repair Service for Panther Units	
D 635/50	Armoured Vehicles in Dust, Heat and Mud	8	Fire Prevention and Firefighting in the Panther	
D 659/2a	Tank Loading	9	Driver, how do you adjust the steering?	
D 659/4	Tank Recovery		Technical Information for Weaponry	
D 659/5	Automatic Fire Extinguishing in Tanks	1 u. 1a	Technical Description of the 75mm KwK 42	
D 659/12	School for Vision	2	Handling and Maintenance of the Turret and Turret Fittings	
D 659/50	The Tank in Winter	3	Guidelines for Gunnery Training	
D 659/51	The Tank Driver in Winter	4	Your Weaponry in the Winter	
D 2003	75 mm KwK 42 Tank Gun	5	What should the Commander know about Weapon Calibration?	
HDv 119/325	Provisional Range Table for the 75mm KwK 42	6	Operational Instructions, Maintenance and Repair of the Fluid Drive	
HDv 481/55	Recognition Pamphlet for Ammunition of the 75mm KwK 42	7	Loading Plan for Arms and Equipment	
D 613/12	Instructions for Radio Communication for Tank Units		Technical Information for the Wireless Radio Systems	
D 949/2	The 10W Transmitter VHF c	1	Lesson Plans for Radio Training	
D 988/2	The VHF Receiver e	4	Radio Communications in the Panther Company	
D 1012/1	The Radio and On Board Communication System	5	Tactical Use of 2 Radio Receivers	
HDv 469/2a	Tank Recognition – Russia	7	Experimental Sand Table Radio Exercise for Commander Training	
HDv 469/2b	Tank Recognition – England and America	8	Teaching Considerations for Radio Communications	
HDv 469/3b	Tank Range Table	11	What should the Commander know about the Gyroscopic Course Indicator?	
HDv 469/4	Tank Fighting at Close Quarters	13	Interference of VHF Waves by the Enemy and Corrective Action	
HDv 470/5e	Training Guidelines	14	Effects of Terrain on the VHF Ground Wave	
HDv 470/20	Manual of Tank Gunnery	16	What the Commander should know about the On Board Radio Communication System	
HDv 316	Engineer Units for All Arms	19	Aircraft Signals and Recognition	
		20	What the Radio Operator should know about Wireless Telegraphy	
		22	Guidance for Inspection of the Radio and On Board Communication System	
		23	Cooperation of Commander and Radio Operator in Combat	
		25	Battle Group Training and Wireless Radio	

Images		Training tables for Panther
655/ 1 u. 5		Oil Pressure Pump and System
655/ 2a u.13		Regenerative Steering
655/ 2b u.14		Steering Brakes and Final Drive
655/ 3		Oil Pressure Activation for Steering Clutch
655/ 4 u. 9		Transmission
655/ 6 u. 7		Running Gear
655/ 8		Idler Wheel with Suspension Mounting
655/10a u. b		Turret Transmission
655/11		Main Clutch
655/12		Gearbox
655/15 a — f		Power Flow
655/16a — f		Use of Steering
655/17		Fuel System
655/18		Cooling System
655/25		Turret
655/26		Commander's Cupola and Breech Discharge Mechanism
655/27		Turret Traverse
655/28		Gun Elevation
655/31		Cutaway View of Gun Barrel
655/32		Air Recuperator
655/33		Operational Instructions for the Air Recuperator
655/34 u. 37		Operational Instructions for the Recoil Buffer
655/35		Breech Locking
655/36		Operational Instructions for Breech Locking
		Action after Firing
655/38		Firing Circuit
657/ 1 — 3		Double Downdraught Carburettor
658/ 1 — 2		Engine HL 230 P 30
660/ 1 — 10		Recognition for all Enemy Tanks

Order through the Army Ordnance Stores Depot, Kassel

Education

Wilhelm Busch		*Critique of the Heart*
		Appearance and Being
Christian Morgenstern		*Gallows Songs, Palmström*
Freiherr von Münchhausen		*Ballads and Songs*
Eugen Roth		*Humans*
		The Woman in World History
		The Miracle Doctor

Order in any good bookshop

To be ordered by: Field Units at Field Order Posts, Depot Units, Training Schools and Courses of the Commander of the German Armoured Corps

Testimonials can be directed to the Inspector of the Armoured Troops, Fehrbelliner Platz 4, Wilmersdorf, Berlin and are viewed by the Tank Training Course in Erlangen

1. Erlangen is a city in Germany where tank training took place. It refers to the documents/training material used during their training in Erlangen.

Wer wird nicht eine Vorschrift loben?
Doch wird sie jeder lesen? – Nein!
Wir wollen weniger erhoben
Und fleißiger gelesen sein.

G. E. Lessing [1]

Die Panther-Fibel [2]

PUBLISHED ON 1ST JUNE 1944 BY THE INSPECTOR
GENERAL OF THE GERMAN ARMOURED CORPS

1. Who would not praise an instruction book? But would they read it? I guess not! We'd rather this praising was not undertaken
And these books were actually read a lot. G.E. Lessing, 2. *The Panther Primer*.

1. Five years the war's been in existence,
Now victory waves from a distance.
We want to and we will succeed,
With weapons good and strong indeed,
So shooting, radioing and driving,
Over the years they've been thriving.
Keep your chin up, man in the tank,
To be better, German soldier of rank,
To be tougher, able and disciplined,
Learn from this book and you will win.

The Panther Primer's now authorised,
Who doesn't know it, it's their demise.
Guderian

Undeterred was Siegfried as a knight,
He went to the woods for a dragon fight.
But there he found with a wicked giggle
A wingless dragon, vile in its wriggle.
But master Siegfried was never afraid
And from his sheath took out his blade.
And raised it up in one swoop fell,
Took off the dragon's head as well.
Through the bushes did the dragon's blood

Flow appetisingly fresh and good.
Siegfried considered, I'll need that, hurry!
I'd better scurry into this slurry.
Blood is a special condensate,
It tans my skin in armour plate.
Bulletproof against lance and sword,
Its worth to me can't be ignored.
Quick, Siegfried, happy and light-hearted
Took off his sword and helm, and started
As God made him – he was in the nudd'
To bathe now in the dragon's blood.
But through the air from somewhere around
A lime tree leaf fluttered down.
It landed on his back-quarter section,
Impeding care for his complexion.

So did Siegfried's dragon-scale armour
Have a hole, but thankfully not larger.
Siegfried laughed at this little mishap,
What can lay into me through this gap?
I'm used to fighting at the anterior,
My good side will be on the exterior.
I pray this unto the stars above,
From the front I know I'm safe thereof!

Die Kunde vom Lindenblatt[1]

Imbibing from a watering hole,
He forgot his weakness, lost control.
Through the tree leaf doing wrong
He'd been killed, although he was strong.
And this is how, says the narrator,
It's dangerous to be an inebriator.
But Siegfried's story's like a slaughter,
He forgot himself drinking water.
As your teacher I show you his remains,
So you can compare and use your brains.

1. Tidings from a lime tree leaf.

This is the same for the Panther tank,
It's vital it never changes, let's be frank.
Invincible from the front, in fact,
But delicate from the side and back.
So do what clever people do
And always show the best side of you!
Women, for example, will agree
On your flaws and idiosyncrasies.
But you first have to recognise
Your weaknesses with expert eyes.
Then you'll be a winner, sure is this,
For your Panther do not remiss.
Expert eyes upon the clock hands
Of 11 to 1 as the traverse pans.
Keep it to around midday,
No damage, then, you'll be okay.

...sonst schlägt's
"13"[1]

Any other time you'll get a breach
From 3000 metres out of reach.
So here the space in between
Is like the lime tree leaf so green.
The leaf is where you're vulnerable,
The clock's where you're impenetrable.
Driver, note when a round's released
And turn fast towards the foe, this beast!
Gunners turn the gun traverse now
So it fires upon the midday hour.
Like the clock's hourly chime
Bongs to show the correct time.
You, commander, turn without fuss
As if your Panther's a Sturmgeschütz.
Oh, Panther crew, always have in mind
Siegfried showing his front, never his behind!

Look at this – the Panther is facing
forward, on the clock face.
This is the range in which a T-34 can
shoot at you.
This danger zone, where the gun
can fire at you, can be a bit smaller
or a bit larger, but it is the area
covered by this lime tree leaf.
Your front is safe, so always fight
from the front.
Don't let anyone get around into
your tree leaf; turn the tank around
until your enemy is out front.
Fire only along the red lines.

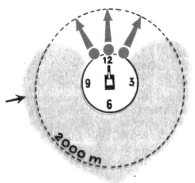

1. Otherwise you hit '13'.

2

Really drunk on some red wine,
Slowcoach is in a dream so fine.
All is well, he feels serene,
So merrily goes to the cinema screen,
For cultural reasons (he's a keen learner)
And to swoon so much for Ilse Werner.
The cinema's size is so tremendous,
So much so, the perspective's horrendous.
The Film Board's showing is all at sea,
The whole thing's too small, oh dear me.
To move onto the next row up
He's got to hoof it a thousand foot.

In front of Slowcoach a man so tall,
Past whom he can't see bugger all,
Pointless to even strain his neck,
It's much better to use some tech.
He who's a **kilometre away** from him
Has a back only 1 **metre slim**.
So if Slowcoach makes a bit of effort
He'll be able to see a little better.
This fellow's back is quite thickset,
Slowcoach can't see a thing just yet.
His view is still quite obscured
But change will soon have to occur.

Two rows down, Slowcoach's curiosity
Spots another huge monstrosity.
Down another 1000 strides
There's another chap, a further metre wide.
So does cover this wrongdoer
2 metres over **2000**, not fewer.
And at **3000** sits a **third**
And then a fourth, how absurd.
Number 5 at **5000**, et cetera,
Blind spot increases, not getting better.
And up on the screen far away,
Ilse Werner's covered totally.

Ein Traum von Ilse Werner[1]

He wakes up squiffy, very miserable,
Hungover, he thinks just is that possible?
A back can cover, at breakneck speed,
The whole cinema screen indeed.
His musings gave no explanation,
The experience only protestation.

SO:

the same back covers:

1 metre at a distance of 1000 metres
2 metres at a distance of 2000 metres
3 metres at a distance of 3000 metres
And so on...

WHY?

1. A Dream of Ilse Werner, popular wartime Dutch-German actress and singer.

Wie breit ist ein Strich?[1]

140 Strich[2]

Nobody spoils it, they just can't work it out.

Kant

What is a line? We know precisely:
The army regulations say concisely.
But when it comes to a hypothesis,
One will get it, the other 50 miss.

Our friend Clever Clogs, he's as bright
As a penny, he shows insight.
'Close one eye, arm stretched from thee.
What, covered by your thumb, can you see?'

Up front less, in the distance more,
To understand it, it's not hardcore.
That you can see on every side
In field of vision far and wide,

What was in the cinema a short while ago.
This room was much narrower though.
Your field of vision everywhere
1000 metres longer than wide there.

So take good care, know the sign;
Your field of vision defines the line.

Das ist ein Strich[3]

◄----1000m----►

Using a thumb as a sight
Measures 40 lines, all right?
It covers one kilometre well
At 40 metres, in a nutshell.

In Civvy Street, a line's extent
Is about one tenth of a percent.

That means he measures on the scale
Exactly one thousandth in detail.
Three decimal points from the sum,
The soldier has the distance done:

At 4500 m, a line is 4.5 m
At 700 m, a line is 0.7 m

I get it now, says Slowcoach, yes,
What the line is, I profess.
One at a thousand metres stands
And then another metre advanced.
For every 1000 metre by there
Is every line one metre wider.

Anyone can work it out,
3000 metres, what about
At 800, five lines there are
Exactly 4 metres and voila.

Distance = 800 m
1 lines = 800 m: 1000 = 0.8 m
5 lines = 5 x 0.8 = 4 m

2000 metres, the width of a thumb
Is 80 metres across, always the sum.
Now it's easy and such joy
To work out distance with this new toy.

1. How wide is a line?, 2. 40 line = Minute of Angle
(MOA: Minute of Angle), 3. This is the line.

Wir messen die **Zielgröße** [1]

Binoculars, through which you look
For a bearing, in lines it's split up:

The eyepiece in the gunsight ahead,
Not lines but triangles instead:

Of course, every child would know
How wide and high these shapes do go.
You already know the top pointy bits
4 lines away from each other sit.
And the height, you notice this too,
The big one's 4, the smaller is 2.

Get a match, take it in your mitt,
Like with the thumb, hone in on target.
The thickness of the match you'll see
The shapes, it fills the gaps between
And when the match is turned sideways,
Same height as the big shape always.

Here's Slowcoach now, he's out again
For 5 cigars, needs to obtain
His favourite brand called 'Coffin Nails',
A thousand for 400 bob in sales.
He works it out:

1000 cigars cost 400 Marks
1 cigar 400 : 1000 = 0.4 Marks
so 5 cigars is 5 x 0.4
= <u>2 Marks</u>

...Child's play!
Going through it line by line It isn't that difficult to define:

You know the distance,
For example, 400

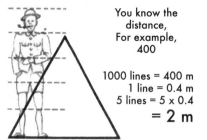

1000 lines = 400 m
1 line = 0.4 m
5 lines = 5 x 0.4
= 2 m

At 400 stands a country chap,
Then with the big shape you can map
And compare the height of your prey
To work out the height in lines okay.

The target measures 5 lines
At a distance of 400 metres
1 line = 400 : 1000 = 0.4 m
5 lines = 5 x 0.4 m = 2 m

So it's easy and a treat
To work out height and width complete.
See a target in your gun sight,
You'll know the distance then, all right.

You can turn it round, the equation,
It can be preferable on occasion.
When you know the target's size,
Then the distance can be surmised.
With this you just don't need to be
A mathematics professor with a degree.

1. We measure the size of the target, 2. 5 cigars = 1 packet of 'Coffin Nails', No! 1/1000 of a pack of 'Coffin Nails' So it is 400 Marks in sales.

Wir messen die **Zielweite**[1]

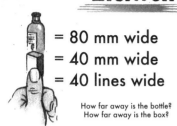

= 80 mm wide
= 40 mm wide
= 40 lines wide

How far away is the bottle?
How far away is the box?

A box of matches has been located,
You must keep your eyes fixated:
'Close one eye, arm stretched from thee
Go back and forth until you see
That the box is covered by your thumb,

Measure a metre's distance in sum.'
Get a bottle of beer, please don't consume,
2 metres away, put it there, give it room.
Its width is now twice as much,
As well as distance, it is as such.
(With empty bottles, double the space
But that's because you're off your face.)

Because our thumbs are quite chunky
The measurement seems like it's clunky.
But forty lines within compressed,
Thumbs up and just make a guess.
This guess can be, though, very acute,
The German Army's new salute.

3 marks has Slowcoach just expended,
A pack of 6 'Coffin Nails', Brazilian
blended. Now he would really like to know
What a thousand are in dough.

6 cigars cost 3 Marks
So one cigar costs:
3 Marks : 6 = 0.5 Marks and
1000 cigars cost 0.5 M x 1000
= 500 Marks

Divided once, then three zeroes on,
It can be done by anyone.
Calculations are not a craft,
That time at school now seems daft.

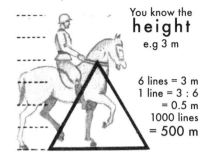

You know the
height
e.g 3 m

6 lines = 3 m
1 line = 3 : 6
 = 0.5 m
1000 lines
= 500 m

It's as easy with thumbs as through the sight,
Like with the ciggies, the maths is right.
If you know the **size** in **metres** true
Of your target in the sights can you
Work out using the big triangle sign
The size translated into lines.
Within these lines, the metres are split
Into a 1000, understand this bit:
To know the size, what a delight,
To work out the range and get it right.

So this succeeds, notice tonight,
Of every target: width and height.

If you don't understand all this,
You'll mess your measurements and miss.

1. We measure the target's range.

6

A person's heart begins to beat
To the pages of pink letter sheet.
On the paper, the ink swirls:
'From the bottom of my heart, dear girl.'
As it says, can this be the start?
Stop, Slowcoach, you're going too far!
'My gracious, dear Miss Gwendoline!'
No, that's not up to the job therein.
He needs a third alternative,
Not keen or too conservative.
A golden mean, nicely blended:
'My dear lady,' that sounds splendid.
This golden mean's not just in the heart,
Elsewhere it also plays a part.

When you write to your soulmate, Style
is the method, like when you estimate...

. . . and this is how it's done:

First estimate what is too far,
The smallest options that there are.
The right one's in the middle, purported,
A bit closer, then you'll have it sorted.
One thousand is a bit too much,
More than 800's about right as such.
So on 900, there you land,
The distance guessed has gone as planned.

Der Liebesbrief [1]

The spring sunset pink is like a rose,
The ersatz coffee inspires your prose.
In the evenings you write, full of feeling,
But mornings leave your sweetheart reeling.
Mornings you write objective and terse,
For your girl in the evenings, but it makes it
worse.

Terrain, time and situation
You must add these to your calculations.

. . . Therefore:

With light-coloured targets and sunshine,
When it's light behind, all fresh and fine.
Look through the sight and at the lines,
What's in between, you can't define.
Guess too short, you'll miss the sign.
At dusk, the evening at twilight
With moving air, fog misty white,
The sun is on the opposite side,
Murk and haze intensified.
Guess shorter – the range is amplified.
An estimation, when you're wrong
Can be either too short or too long.
But guess first too short, then too far,
The golden mean and you'll be a superstar!

1. The love letter.

In front of Troy, as fate revealed,
Achilles met, on the battlefield
The queen of all the Amazons.
A duel, he thinks, I'll get right on.
Amazed at first, he then felt weak
As he clapped eyes on her physique.
More angel than a person at all
But the queen had frailties and could fall.
So we must see, have it all at hand,
What Achilles himself must understand.

History puts things under a magnifying glass.
Here we've copied a little story.

For all the tank types we have here
There's always the same key idea.
Recruits, they learn in their first year
To keep hair on and keep head clear.
Get the enemy up close, on the attack
Until you can give that one good thwack.
Give him a nip, then increase it a lot,
Test him with a body shot.
How's it going, keep an eye on it too,
What'll you do to him, or him to you?
Profile, will he tighten the noose?
Hit his weak points with a bang, loose!
A tank can explode into many sections
If you know the type and its imperfections.

Look up the tank firing table and the recognition charts, which
are found in the back of this book.

1. Panthersilea.

8

To the fight, the queen brings a lass
In case anything should come to pass.
Achilles, likewise, brings a friend
To keep the girl away his end.
Achilles with strength unabated,
This queen bee has him frustrated.
The royal woman did then wield
And got his flesh under his shield.
He retreated to the reserves,
Above all just to calm his nerves.
He didn't show where he's been hit,
(The heel, for him, is a sensitive bit.)
Achilles gets closer to his foe
To reach with his sword, to and fro,
So know for cover and advance,
Two different things for importance:

You, Diomedes, go and
slay here. I'll stay here.
Achilles

Take cover until you can say
I can attack without delay
So here he goes, give 'em some lead,
Shooting at what's up ahead.
Secondly, attacks will misfire
If they occur without covering fire.
Mostly, tanks are not independent,
They go at least with one other attendant.
But even two sidekicks, thick as thieves,
Won't miss a trick or be deceived.
Watched over by the rest of your kin
Until you've done the enemy in.
But only show your front (best) side,
Think of Siegfried's weak bit of his hide.
Smartly exploit what your enemy lacks
So do to him what he'd do back.
He'll be ready to start a scuffle
But won't quite believe all the kerfuffle.
For every surprise attack
Gives your advance extra thwack.

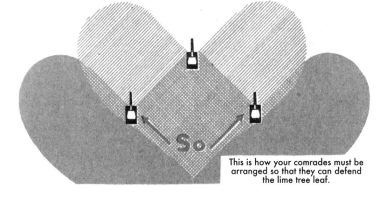

This is how your comrades must be
arranged so that they can defend
the lime tree leaf.

There's no doubt you'll draw a blank
When in battle on the right flank.
In a sword fight pick up an old blade
But later your luck changes grade.
Go for it up front, take a chance,
Genteel and posh, a country dance.
Later a lady is after you,
From behind she did pursue.
Today flirtation comes from the side,
In a motor this can be done with pride.
It's crucial that you recognise,
At this moment, there is the prize.

So fåhrt dein Feind –[1]

moving diagonally

approaching

favourable

unfavourable

moving across

favourable

moving diagonally

unfavourable

leaving

favourable

Das ift dein Panther[2]

The situation, time and gradation,
But unlike the fight, no alteration.
In the real world, it starts so urgent,
The enemy and setting can be divergent.
He gets right up into your face;
How far? (See information here just in case).
Dead opposite is the right place.
Can show him your side this time
But the back is definitely not a crime.
He'll shoot at you, firing on cue,
And much more tricky it'll be too.
He's coming diagonally, all askew,
Stay centred to unnerve,
Turret fixed onto the curve.
Note here that every shot tried on,
It's best for it to land side-on.

1. The way your enemy drives, 2. This is your Panther.

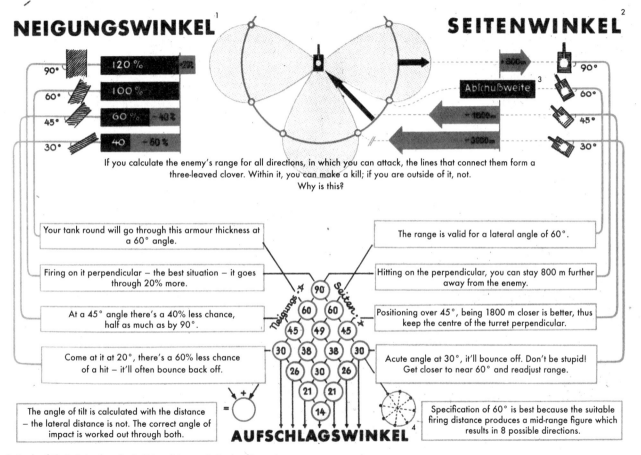

NEIGUNGSWINKEL[1]

SEITENWINKEL[2]

90°	120 % +20%
60°	100 %
45°	60 % −40%
30°	40 −60 %

90°
Abschußweite[3]
60°
← 800m
45°
← 1800m
30°
← 3000m

If you calculate the enemy's range for all directions, in which you can attack, the lines that connect them form a three-leaved clover. Within it, you can make a kill; if you are outside of it, not.
Why is this?

Your tank round will go through this armour thickness at a 60° angle.

The range is valid for a lateral angle of 60°.

Firing on it perpendicular — the best situation — it goes through 20% more.

Hitting on the perpendicular, you can stay 800 m further away from the enemy.

At a 45° angle there's a 40% less chance, half as much as by 90°.

Positioning over 45°, being 1800 m closer is better, thus keep the centre of the turret perpendicular.

Come at it at 20°, there's a 60% less chance of a hit — it'll often bounce back off.

Acute angle at 30°, it'll bounce off. Don't be stupid! Get closer to near 60° and readjust range.

Neigungs-✗ 90 *Seiten-✗*
60 60
45 49 45
30 38 38 30
26 30 26
21 21
14

The angle of tilt is calculated with the distance — the lateral distance is not. The correct angle of impact is worked out through both.

Specification of 60° is best because the suitable firing distance produces a mid-range figure which results in 8 possible directions.

AUFSCHLAGSWINKEL[4]

1. Angle of tilt, 2. Lateral angle, 3. Firing distance, 4. Angle of impact.

Before the battle he's weighed up
The girl, with bows and arrows well made up.
Riding her horse, second to none,
Her javelin throw is not to be outdone.
At close quarters, a battle provoked,
Her chances too are now revoked.
Achilles the hero unsurpassed,
Enemies even say this, staying steadfast.
As weapons he chooses sword and shield,
The princess has been brought to heel.
Blows rain down, he's in overdrive,
Achilles fights to stay alive.
There are the first signs of fading,
The queen's ability is degrading.

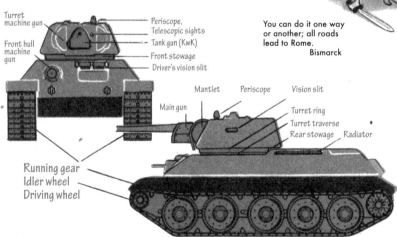

You can do it one way
or another; all roads
lead to Rome.
                    Bismarck

This is what happens when tanks clash:
One thing works, one thing is dashed.
So if with armour piercing nothing gives
Then simply try the high explosives.
But all of the emphasis must sit
On gun, running gear, optics, vision slit.
Explosives work, they are stunning,
Destroys completely or stops them running.
In any case, make it a total wreck,
Get the turret and snap its neck.
Hit the back, elegantly à la mode
To make the exhaust fully explode.
Success depends on a good two out of three
But make the right choice for AP or HE.

Turret machine gun
Front hull machine gun

Periscope, Telescopic sights
Tank gun (KwK)
Front stowage
Driver's vision slit

Mantlet   Periscope   Vision slit
Main gun
                    Turret ring
                    Turret traverse
                    Rear stowage   Radiator

Running gear
Idler wheel
Driving wheel

O.V. [1]

Non so viel [2]

sharp bits of shrap-
nel will hit as you
go further out in
metres square.
Although one bit is just
enough for the fattest
of the fat Tommies.

Carbide has made his guts distend;
A bang – an explosion out the back end.
From the guts, to the sides and up ahead
The pressure soon begins to spread.
The force meanwhile to the head increases,
Blowing it into little pieces.
The boots, of course, they stay standing
Keeping upright upon landing.
The pressure's gone to the front and sides
Leaving not much else besides.

As in this case on its way,
The blast explodes without delay.
This is how the explosion goes
When it's 10 metres in front of your nose.
It can't be helped by any means,
You'll be blown into smithereens.
From far away it's best to deliver
The shot away from all the slivers.
To avoid shrapnel all entangled,
Make sure you fire at an angle.

M.V.

If you are on clear, hard ground with solid turf, frozen mud or
ice, you can fire a ricochet shot. In that way, the shrapnel flies
10m high into foxholes and trenches. Use a delay fuse when
under 50m. In mud, snow, loose sand, this does not work.

If you fire with a delay fuse at perpendicular walls, wooden huts, defence bunkers in
the ground, and lightly fortified positions, then there are no sharp splinters, but the
shot goes straight in and the whole thing blows up into the air. The target will go up
like it has hit a mine. You should not shoot with a delay fuse at hard walls! It won't
detonate and a dud will bounce off.

1. OV, Ohne Verzögerung (without delay) and MV, Mit Verzögerung (with delay), 2. From this.

Achilles goes in with all his might
Where she seems not at all quite right.
He's spotted that her arm is tired
So he hits her as much as is required.
He becomes aware that she is wheezing;
She's weakening now, her senses easing.
After a tough fight of 16 rounds
She's finally been taken down.
With tanks this is commonplace,
On the ground this is the case.
Look at each one of the shots
To see how you've hit, and what.

Then you notice: here it's a bit weak
So you have a little peek.
You've hit the target but he's endured,
I'll tell you now, be assured.
Go on now without a care,
Your tank gun gives them all a scare.
You've made a good hit with the shell,
You've really given that chap hell.
Hit after hit, thunder and lightning,
But unless you're accurate, it's only frightening.
So through the visor ascertain,
Learn it, as this book will pertain.

THESE ARE THE SHOTS INTO TANK ARMOUR AT:

90°   60°   45°   30°

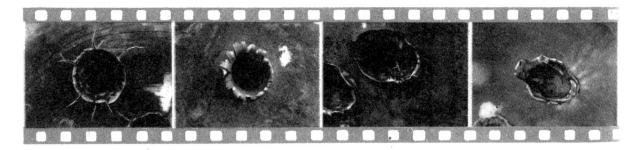

Wie knackt die Pz.Granate Panzerplatten? So: [1]

It will hit the plate in less than 1/10000 of a second and then the igniter explodes the round in the inside of the vehicle. It has the effect of complete destruction. There are no failures!

Here are the slow-motion images – a delicacy for connoisseurs!

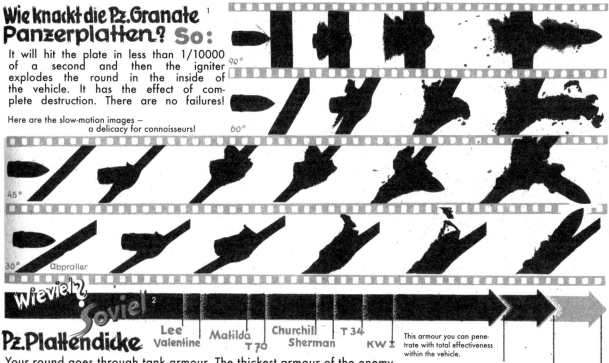

Pz.Plattendicke

Your round goes through tank armour. The thickest armour of the enemy tanks in the field is shown here. The differences in capability and material are calculated within.

You have a wonderful reserve of power against all enemies. And also against any future ones! For they can't make their armour any thicker.

This armour you can penetrate with total effectiveness within the vehicle.

With this thickness, the inner pieces and screws fly off, welded joints tear apart, driving gear is broken and equipment fails.

Anyway, it's a moral thing.

1. How does the AP round hit armour plating? So:, 2. How thick is the armour? This much

Die erschröckliche Bärbl[1]

Labels in illustration: Wucht 2, Schwerkraft 3, Luftwiderstand 4

Back in the year dot, the good old days indeed,
When the tempestuous Kaiser was Gottfried.
When August the Cast-Iron ruled the roost,
It was great fun – the campaigns were introduced.
They shot with cannons and the 'Fiery Greta',
Now they're in the armoury, antiques no better.
From canvas sacks you put the powder in
And then stick the cannonball down within.
The field commander checks through his scope
The enemy's layout, if there's any hope.
And so fire is started, setting off the flint,
Mostly it's all over after an hour's stint.
With loud cracks and bangs, the cannonball showers,
Stuckmeyster gazes at this for hours.
Berthold the Black, a monk, who pioneered
This gunpowder that today is revered.

But the shot has such little speed,
Baron Munchausen can hop on indeed
Onto the ball, straight out of the barrel.
Yes, that was possible – there was no peril.
It didn't run straight, trajectory was terrible,
Gravity pulled it down, it's so unbearable.
Not a surprise then – a very slow flight,
Elongated, slow, takes about a fortnight
To go to the heavens, into the atmosphere,
Getting battered or dented was a great fear.
'The terrifying lass' was reduced to tears
But she's a buxom gal, no problem there.
Cannonballs, well they're rather curvy,
Air resistance sends them a bit topsy-turvy.
The force against it, compresses its path,
And all in one go, I'll show you the maths!

1. The terrifying lass, 2. Force, 3. Gravity, 4. Air resistance.

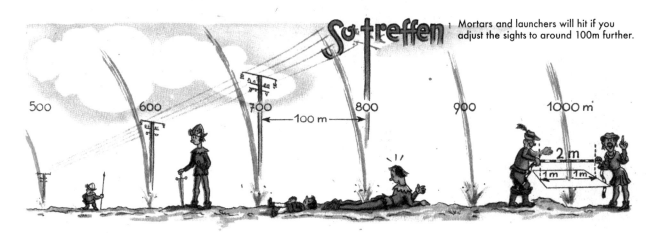

So treffen [1]

Mortars and launchers will hit if you adjust the sights to around 100m further.

500   600   ←—100 m—→   700   800   900   1000 m

2 m
1m   1m

Stationary targets will be hit if the range is accurately calculated on the instruments. **The height of the target does not matter!**

You must use high explosive rounds to produce the desired effect. Low-lying targets are easier to hit. **Width and target length are important!**

To hit a target over 2 metres in size, you must estimate it to 1 metre. Only having the correct trajectory will hit the target: **calculate the exact range in your sights!**

As you can see, they go in an arc,
They trail from above to hit their mark.
See the interconnected telegraph poles,
One after the other, playing their roles.
With one hundred metres in between them,
The range you'll grasp, more than by rule of thumb.
Then whether a target's down low or up high,
Nothing else works; you must measure and verify.

You'll hit targets easier when they're lying low
But later on they can be higher up, though.
Using your sights, a direct hit,
Will only come from accurately measuring it.
With errors a shot will just drop short
Giving your enemy only mild discord.
Even in the Holy Roman Empire
Using sights and range was still required.

1. To hit.

Die schlanke KwK [1]

Wucht [2]

Luftwiderstand [4]

Schwerkraft [3]

Trajectory's no longer a modern idea,
Tank guns shoot far and near.
Gunpowder's power today is strong
But it gives off a hell of a pong!
Prowls through the barrel of almost endless size
Like Caracciola on the grid, racing motorised.
The heavy round with the greatest speed,
Without a doubt, it will succeed.
For **a**, is not what it was before,
It's very light, it's not a chore.
And **b**, understands the force of gravity;
It zings up into the air with concavity.
With arms and legs, gravity draws it out
Because falling down's time we could do without.
And **c**, there is the air resistance
Running over everything with persistence.

And **d**, our rascal tank round, like a drill,
As if thinner than air, it'll punch through at will.
So the round doesn't spin in somersaults,
Finding it spinning for days, not coming to a halt.
To keep its path ideal and direct,
Straight across, like a ruler, is correct.
Without that old-fashioned high arched curve,
Now flies straight to the target without a swerve.
One on top of the other like electricity wire
Not like the poles split at 100m prior.
No, it's as thin as musical notation,
A line apart, you'll notice in this situation.

andante cantabile un poco con moto

Al - le Vö - gel sind scho - on da! [5]

1. The slim KwK, KwK=Kampfwagenkanone (fighting vehicle cannon), 2. Force, 3. Gravity, 4. Air resistance, 5. All the birds are here already!

So treffen[1]

A shot from the KwK will hit if you adjust the sight to about 100m further.

1 Strich = auf 500m = 50m

Low-lying targets will only be hit if the range is correct on the instruments. **Width and length do not matter!**

You can't miss stationary targets. The direct hit shot will sit on an interval of 1 line on top of it. **Elevation is important!**

At 500 metres, all 50 centimetres will be a hit. A 2 metre high target can be hit 4 times. You can estimate around 200 metres above and below **if the amount the sights are showing is greater than the range!**

Indeed, low-lying targets are hard to hit well
Because your shot flies parallel.
But stationary targets are pretty easy;
Out of them all, they're bright and breezy.
Don't stand up straight (be supine),
Like von Goetzen and Wallenstein.
There's a fixed target, what a relief,
For anything there shouldn't cause you much grief.

But for anything that gives you nerves,
There's not just one sight setup, there are reserves.
One of these keeps the dial consistently
Always the same as the range will be.
The other sights they are bigger without exception
And these sights hit better in perception.
But notice that in the Great German domain
Sights and range were not always the same.

1. How to hit.

1600
1500
1400
1300
1200
1100
1000

1 Strich 2

Die **Trefferleiter** 1

→ No longer is a hit

These sight lines will hit all!

→ Doesn't hit

=Lowest note = Lowest sight line = Correct range All the little birds...

Al = le Vög - lein sind schon...

Let's put a target on a chart,
And fix the pointers on, ready to start.
Shoot at it, but after every hit
Move 100 metres further out from it.
Then like a ladder, up you climb,
Shots go up the steps in time.
Sitting nicely upon each rung,
Distance is each line where the HE's sprung.
But for AP ammo, however,
Go up just half for each rung and level.
You'll soon find out, as we go on,
Why this is so gratifying thereupon.
But we look at this whole place first
Just for the shells with the explosive outburst.

So play a string on the violin,
You'll soon see it wears a little thin.
But up higher up the scale you can climb,
Smash through the ladder whole this time.
But don't try to figure out musical notes,
They're more difficult to denote.
The scale of direct hits, here we are,
The sights are positioned all afar.
Alongside what we want to hit
And the distances, so you'll get it.
Building upon the musical root,
Musically where you'll shoot.
There's the scale, there's nothing finer,
Work over it, in major or minor.

Apex, the key, the path of least resistance,
(Keep on firing!) It's the distance!
Direct hit! Smaller you make the sights,
It won't work out quite right.
The whole scale is within the sight's dial,
Matching up with distance all the while.
To get a full hit with great style
Have the base point, the root, all in profile.
The other rungs lay above,
With the sights as well thereof.
The number of rungs is as much
As the lines for our target as such.
For every rung, a sight line in scope,
The gap: a line! We shoot in hope!
(Up to 1200m, you'll cope!)

1. The hit parade, 2. line = Minute of Angle (MOA: Minute of Angle).

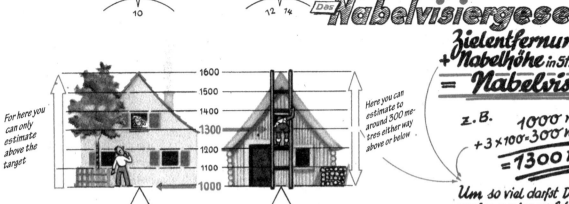

Das Nabelvisiergesetz:
Zielentfernung
+ Nabelhöhe in Strich × 100
= Nabelvisier

z.B. 1000 m
+ 3 × 100 = 300 m
= 1300 m [2]

Um so viel darfst Du Dich rauf u. runter verschätzen!

For here you can only estimate above the target

Here you can estimate to around 300 metres either way above or below

1600
1500
1400
1300
1200
1100
1000

Firing under the rungs on view,
Is he who shoots without a clue.
Because he has not set the sights to see
What the distance to there might be. But
when it's right, use your foot
To keep point of aim, then kaputt.
But estimate short by only a little space,
Of your impact there'll be no trace. A
good hit, one that's well known, Sits in
the middle, not at each end alone. So
always fix, I say forthright, The centre
of the target within your sights. Goes
high and far for the drop But it rarely
ends up as a flop.

When the estimation's not exact,
You'll still make the hit, in fact:
Per one hundred metres, too far, too
near, Is a rung on the ladder here.
From centre point, up or down a stripe.
Still a hit! Put that in your pipe..!
And big is the room for manoeuvre,
Up or down, can be a mover.
The centre of the target to you
Is the middle of the sight's view.

1. Measure or estimate, as we here teach,
   How far (exactly) is the target's reach.
   Of your ladder, that is the base,
   Then quickly, does thinking take place.

2. Target in viewfinder then compared
   With the points and lines (all square).
   So the height has been assessed,
   And how many lines for the height expressed. The ladder has so many stepping places, Then does the thought process make haste!

3. So one rung it does say to you,
   Set the sights 100 metres up the queue.
   How many are the rungs you count,
   Up to the centre point, you surmount.
   So then you add one hundred on,
   Onto the range thereupon.

   And with that you're all safe and secure,
   You'll hit the centre, all assured.

but always hold your sights at the bottom edge of a target! not onto the centre!

1. Target estimate rule: Range to the target + Height of the central point (in lines x 100) = Point of focus for sights.
2. There's only so much you can estimate above or below!

Spr.

'All the litt–'

Zielentfernung
+ Zielhöhe in Strich × 100
= Nabelvisier

z.B. 4 × 100 = 400 → 500
                        900

500

900
8
700
6
500

für **PZ. GRANATEN**

Pz.

1300
12
11
10
900
8
7
6
500

1300
12
11
10
900
8
7
6
500

'Fox, you've stolen all the geese'

Always round the height of the target down
to the nearest line!

When the target's **near** and a **large** size,
The ladder has **many** rungs crosswise.
Many sights you can choose,
You won't miss the target, you can't lose.

800
7
6
5
4
300

1700
16
15
14
13
1200

But if the target's **small** and **far-flung**,
The ladder **hasn't many** rungs.
And there are so **fewer** sights
With which to hit the target right.

600
5
400

4000

Measuring a target with only one line,
Accordingly it's not always fine.
And just here, in this case,
There's only one sight in place.
That's just the range that is required,
As in the Holy Roman Empire.
If there's a target of small figuration
For example, near your location,
You can't get yourself into a mess,
You can however make a better guess.
If it's far away, as a rule,
Make a mark and sharpen your tools.
If far away, you'll shoot without strife,
Use keywords: 'Stain', 'Fork' or 'Knife'.

Firing AP it changes again,
Shots fly flat and low in the main.
And climb up only one half line
For each 100 metres fine.
So has the ladder up to the mid-section,
For AP, as many intersections.
As it had for HE overleaf,
Like a musical leitmotif.
'All the little birds are here' – whistle,
From KwK, shoot AP missile.
But the intervening spaces low and high,
With the 'fox' tune here, half the size.
The rungs here are pretty tight
With AP than by those that set alight.
So to hit the same target right,
Again you have to use your sights.

The narrow rungs, it can be seen,
Again give you the ways and means.
It indicates the space is doubled
So estimating should be no trouble.
So take for now, it's not a chore,
The same type of ladder you used before.
Instead of rungs twice as constricted,
Twice as long the ladder's now depicted.
But don't settle into your old ways
With the centre point in the middle phase.
The turret top is also a part;
Calculate the whole target within the chart.
Put 100 metres down in place
As the distance just in case.
And now – now this is the main gist,
The shot will be again in the midst.

Use your centre point of focus only on targets up to 1200 metres!

1. Spr=Sprenggranate=High Explosive Round, 2. Range to the target + Target elevation (in lines x 100) = Point of focus for sights,
3.Pz. Granaten=Panzergranaten=Armour Piercing Rounds.

Das Anrichten[1]

Here calls Jean, as is observed,
'My lord, dinner is now served'.
The announcement has, not by chance,
A particular kind of importance.
For he who takes Roquefort cheese
And finely seasoned mayonnaise
Piled on paper, what a no-brainer,
Champagne out of a kitchen container,
Goose livers scooped out of a can
They're worse than a barbarian.
When completely savage and wild,
Half as delicious, it tastes vile.
However can an evening meal so fine
And army cider and moonshine
Work much better at any rate,
Served in glasses and on plates.

1. Preparing dinner.

Served that way it is delicious,
Dinner served, so auspicious.
How far away is each glass,
Knives and forks, so first-class.
If on the table cloth so swanky,
Place settings are never wonky.
Jean knows all this with ease;
Senior Court Master of Ceremonies.

Here your target sits still and straight
Upon this sighting point so great.
There are, as always two selections
Through telescope sights circumspection.
2½ is good precision
To see the target in your field of vision.
Big or small in projection
You will see him in perfection.
If you choose dark or light,
In daylight you'll see him just right.
If seen poorly or in brief,
Don't use the sights, they'll give you grief.

The telescope, looking through
The **machine gun** has moved its view
A metre to the left, make sure you've eyed
Things a metre to the left alongside.
The optics for your **KwK**
Are however measured to convey
A third of a metre from straight
So keep things left to compensate.
At fifteen hundred and any more,
The spin with HE is too severe.
So to stop this all from going wrong,
Instead stay one line left along.

23

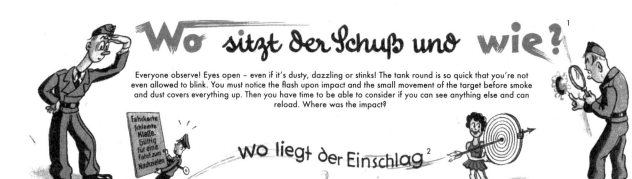

Wo sitzt der Schuß und wie? [1]

Everyone observe! Eyes open – even if it's dusty, dazzling or stinks! The tank round is so quick that you're not even allowed to blink. You must notice the flash upon impact and the small movement of the target before smoke and dust covers everything up. Then you have time to be able to consider if you can see anything else and can reload. Where was the impact?

wo liegt der Einschlag [2]

not on target but...

on target but...

Then you're at fault – maybe you'll do better next time. Only observe the source of the cloud of smoke from the explosion. Does it cover the target? Or was it in front? Which way is the wind blowing? If you couldn't see the explosion then it is likely it hit the land around it. Place your next shot with good visibility. If there's been a ricochet, make a kink in the trajectory. If you've fired a dud, fire once again. You must compare the placing of the impact with that of the target, the distance in metres, the spacing of the lines in the sighting equipment or estimate the target length.

Then this is the benefit of an accurate weapon. The KwK can specifically fire with precision up to 2000 metres. Then up to 3000 metres, of every three shots, one misses. Over 4000 metres it is only every fourth. Then you must be careful whether your enemy has spotted you or not. A shot bouncing off the tank shouldn't faze you. Just place the next shot on the neighbouring surface, then it should go through. There is no tank that your shot will not penetrate and no target that it cannot reach or finish off

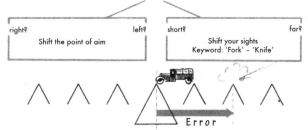

right?	left?	short?	far?
Shift the point of aim		Shift your sights Keyword: 'Fork' – 'Knife'	

Error

If the shot goes to the right or left, you must make a new point of aim from the old one

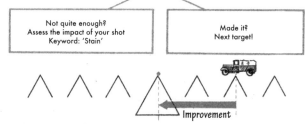

Not quite enough? Assess the impact of your shot Keyword: 'Stain'	Made it? Next target!

Improvement

on the same line segment on which you have already played, or even go at it from the other side. Focus on the next sighting point along, which the target is now sitting on. Note this measurement on the line and set this up for the other targets.

1. Where did the shot hit, and how?, 2. Where was the impact?

The ladder becomes your sixth sense,
The shot will reach the target hence.
No short or long shot will be a surprise,
It'll work hundreds of times you try.
And even if once it doesn't function,
Never change the aim point - a malfunction.

sondern: # Stell das Visier um ! [1]

Denn:

1. With high explosive rounds you must improve twice as much as with armour piercing tank rounds - see the ladder diagram.   Therefore:

2. If you are aiming freely a bit higher or further with the barrel and the impact is not high enough on the target, it won't quite work, even if it looks to be close. Move in between the lines about 100 metres and this can be overcome by a couple of lines on the chart- how much by, your sighting scale will tell you.   Therefore:

3. If you do this correctly, the aiming point will either cover the target or be free-floating.   Therefore:

Wieviel ? Kräftig!
Denn: ## Der Einschlag [2]

is too short...

Here you see trajectories that are exaggeratedly awry if you shoot at a target at a 800m distance with different sight setups. The measurements, although correct, they do not take into account whether the landscape is flat or sloping.

...or is overshot!

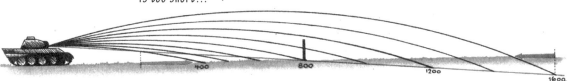

400   800   1200   1600.

The impact is always positioned nearer the target than in the sights. You estimate: **shot is 300** m too far or too short. That makes sense. But: **the sights**... were 400 metres too far or too short. So that you always hit the target: **Change things with gusto!**

1. Otherwise: Reposition your sights! because:, 2. By how much? Powerfully! For: the impact.

With sights spurred on at the start,
But to the impact, a long way apart.
Without a head start he's not competing
Because his power is depleting.
Pistol fired, sights let fly,
Soon the distance isn't far thereby.

With AP rounds, it is only half as bad.
They fly doubly as high and come back
down more steeply.

Impact kept in his sight's visibility,
But then with a superior capability,
Whooshes past like a runner refined,
But leaves the target way behind.
The impact will happen in the end,
If the landscape does ascend.

When firing, the game's the same with it
As long as range **in front of the target**
Is the impact **in front of** the sights,
The target will be hit all right.
But **behind** the target; the impact's weak,
Sights can't keep up, so to speak.

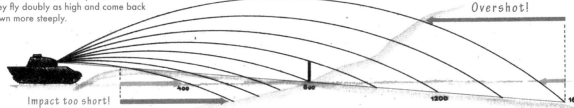

Overshot!

Impact too short!

400   800   1200   1600

You'll mess up a lot less if you take a look at the lay of the land. The impact may hit the target, but the sights would be out by about a few hundred metres.

So:

If you can see along the ground well, the impact will be exactly the distance which is dialled in to the sights. **However:** A short shot hides the target and the target hides a longer overshot! Think in both cases: I can't miss that much! Think! You've still got a way to go.

So:

Sighting in and shooting

1. Estimate the path between the target and impact and confidently add on about a third. If you can see well, add a bit more. That is your room for error.
2. If the sights show too far, deduct a bit from your room for error; if it is too close, add more. That is your range to the target.
3. Use your sights centred (like on the ladder) and shoot again. Now that should do the job. Up to 1200 metres. Any further, shoot with 'Knife' or 'Fork'.

1. The handicap runner.

Fleck

To fill up your glass you'd love to do,
But your aim is all askew.
The outcome is - to your disdain,
The white tablecloth has a stain.
The distance badly calculated,
The wine and the glass are separated.
Put glass over stain, you obscure,
The host doesn't see, you make sure.
Pour yourself another wine,
Now it's in the glass this time.
Now you've taken the right line,
No stain on the cloth so fine.
It's valid not just when you pour
But when you're shooting in the war.

Take the range, which does agree
With the target you there see.
Dial it in just perfect,
In case the distance was correct.
Now we turn the tables round,
This way now should not confound.
First, the place to hit exact
You're holding on for impact.
Now you turn the sights towards
Where you hit, then don't ignore
The range on the sights you read,
Finally computed it indeed.
Distance measured better erstwhile
If you use the rangefinder dial.
However, there is no hope
If you do this on a steep slope.
The point of aim can just change
Making the hit out of range.

If you are firing at a vertical target, there are two elegant ways in which you can hit a particular point.

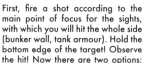

Target

First, fire a shot according to the main point of focus for the sights, with which you will hit the whole side (bunker wall, tank armour). Hold the bottom edge of the target! Observe the hit! Now there are two options:

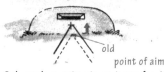

old
point of aim

① Only made a stain: aim as it was for your first shot, and adjust the sight so that the point has reached up towards the target. Now release. You will have the exact distance in your sights.

new

Now you don't need to hold the bottom edge of the target like at the beginning. Let the points settle on what you want to hit (the weakest part of the tank, and so on). You'll hit the exact spot there by the second shot.

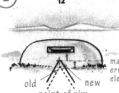

margin for error on elevation

old   new
point of aim

② Or: change the main point of aim. Fire a first shot under the main aiming point, keeping the margin for error on elevation above the point that you want to hit. Let it sit above and the same amount below.

B o t h   t e c h n i q u e s   w o r k   b u t   o n l y   o n   v e r t i c a l   f l a t   t a r g e t s   a n d   w h e n   y o u   h a v e   o b s e r v e d   a   f i r s t   s h o t .

1. The Stain.

Max und Moritz [1]

ein Strich [2]

100 m

When you try to do some good, it seldom
goes as good as it should.

Wilhelm Busch

(From author Wilhelm Busch) Two boys,
Are stealing apples here with joy.
They have, for this whacky idea,
Taken our useful ladder here.
The day is over, it has sprung,
The sun shines through each rung.
Casting shadows on the meadow
The young lad, Max, looks down below.
The lines on which your shots do fall
Are wide as the shadows' sprawl.
What on the ladder were some lines,
On the ground for you it shines.
For a hundred metres is its reach
And hidden in the gap of each
Is each target on which you fire,
When it's less than one line higher.
So for each target to set aglow,
For each, the range you must know.

The Holy Roman Empire, as it was,
Works the same way because
Let's say the ladder changes size,
Each rung a hundred metres high.
It'll seem as it was just now,
Take a measurement as it allows.
Shoot at the target undemanding,
Two shots, of which the second outstanding.
Whatever you want, rearrange,
400 metres further along in range.
So there's 400 line segments,
On the ground it underwent,
The measurements are now inside,
Each of the ladder's' rungs astride.
And so the ladder on the grass
Serves as a tape measure, first class.
On this lovely meadow I can assess
This size quickly and with success.

1. Max and Moritz, 2.1 line.

GABEL [1]

When there's a target all aligned,
See what's in front and what's behind.
It all works out very nice,
Naming this **'Fork'** will suffice.
Just as it's here with Panther steel,
On the dinner table genteel.
You don't quite know if it's correct,
When you eat with a fork direct.

And this looks like:
1. Fire a shot as close as possible.
2. If it was too short, add more range; if it was too long, subtract from the range, an from your 'Fork' measurement too:

HE rounds:	up to 1200 m	200 m	AP rounds:	1200 - 2000 m . . 200 m
	up to 3000 m	400 m		over 2000 m . . 400 m
	over 3000 m	800 m		

The target must lie in between these two shots (the 'Fork').

3. Your next shot is in the middle of the 'Fork'. The target is between the last shot and one of the first, therefore in a 'Fork' that is half the size.
4. The next shot is in the middle of your new 'Fork' and so on, until you make the hit. Now you can slog away.
But always: hold the bottom edge of a target!

Richtiges Visier [2]

There's a difference you can glean
If a target can't be seen.
In the foreground or in the hinterland
You'll need your **'Knife'** close at hand.
And thrust the knife like a slash,
Go for the target in a flash.
Don't confuse this, however,
With 'waving it around madly at whatever'.
Which is why this operation
'Shoots at target without speculation'.
You must often be content
With rungs in only small segments.
But **it is better** if you can,
To the target, get closer than.

1. First, get your shot as close as possible to the target.
2. Place a shot closer to the target; in front or be hind, according to the terrain.
3. Compare with the lines which you've either added on or taken away. These you get from taking readings from missed shots on the ground.

But always: hold the bottom edge of a target!

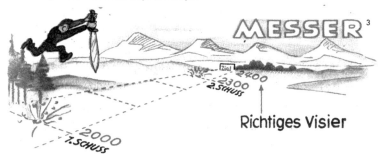

MESSER [3]

Richtiges Visier

1. Fork, 2. Correct Sight setting, 3. Knife.

CIRCUS Mirandola [1]

A family of circus riders looking bright
As a lily, dressed in white,
With coloured pink wide stripes,
Kids in height order like organ pipes.
And due to a lack of finances,
All six on one horse, it dances.
And so they circle with due care
Around the ring on a mare.
She is smooth and brown like cola,
With the modest name of Mirandola.
The troop seem to move towards
Doing a jump on this horse.
Mum starts the run up, go, allez,
You think, hope they make it all the way!
But the moment it began to bound,
Just as they left the ground,
If one properly calculated,
Mirandola's a bit discombobulated.
She bounced up in a daring skip
And the crowd cheered in worship.
She'd hardly put back down a hoof
Then Mr Gemahl went up aloof,
In the air, jumps up, for his life,
He's sat precisely by his wife.
The tempo gets brisker and then brisker,
The kids are jumping by a whisker.
One thinks, this has got to go all wrong,
Amazingly they do it, still going strong.
At the end they're sitting next to each other,
On the pony, behind their mother.
If one jumps as the horse goes near,
Then it will always work, all clear.

Shoot at a target when it's moving,
You need the same kind of proving.
To get a shot right at its prime,
Even if there's not much time.
And within this time duration,
The target's further on in motion.
And this time span is so quick,
The shot goes past, you've missed a trick.
So if you try this artfully:
To shoot right where the target will be.
It's called predicted fire, this is why:
Target drives into it as it goes by.
Shoot when the target's not quite there, Your KwK
tank gun will hit it square!
If target's up to 200 metres away
From your tempo do not sway.
Make a stop, for the round's velocity
At such a range, no virtuosity.
But if it moves further from your gun
Predicted fire is what can be done.

Measuring predicted fire's found
On your sighting lines (on page, look down).
Count where in the row of points
Where the firing point does adjoin.
And then, as is always the case,
Get your main sighting point in place.
Then look upon the pointed rows,
Moving to the middle, the target shows.
And when it reaches the point specific,
You've predicted your fire somewhat
terrific. Open fire and please pay attention:
The middle of the target is the intention.

VORHALT [2]

1. Circus Mirandola, 2. Future position.

30

Then: fire control, put your hands away,
Instead intently do convey,
To be exact, when out front's warlike,
Target sits in the big spike.
And so, look at the prediction,
Correct it if there's a contradiction:
If the **target's** moved a bit **too** far,
Prediction's **added on to** the par.
If the shot goes out of line,
Take some **away from** the pointy spine.
A small bit, if the wrong amount,
From prediction **taken off** the count.

On the path of your target don't be askew,
To your direction, he'll be at an angle to you.
This will turn your calculations,
Meaningless and to negation.
Target hurries on in the blink of an eye,
At an acute angle to you come by.
This demands a correction,
Take only half from your number selection!

too far   +   −   take off

Now this is the next question:
How do I find this number suggestion?
Estimate the target's speed,
This with experience you'll be able to read!
Look up the measurements on the table,
If with maths, you're not too able.
Do it, the calculations are outlined,
Predictions of the old kind.

For every speed you want to know,
You must do some calculations though.
But this is no sorcery:
Guess the speed and divide by three!
The prediction's given a position
Of the line for tank ammunition.
With high explosives, you must ponder:
They take longer to go over yonder.
The measurements you must extend
As it says here, then you amend.
With HE, divide speed by two,
This is the name of the game to you,
Table's been put aside, declined,
Predictions of a new kind.

Moving across

Full calculation

Half calculation

1. Zielgeshwindigkeit = Target speed Pz = AP, Spr = HE 2. Geschwindigkeit = Speed z.b = for example
3. Moving at an angle 4. Moving at an acute angle.

Since Bach and Handel, tuned to repre-
sent The concert pitch, is this instrument.
Before it goes to the concert there,
They make sure it's tuned up with care,
To match the notes of the cellist,
Of the bugle and of the bassist.
And every note that's in the right pitch,
It will then the fugue enrich.
But play without chamber music near,
'All the little birds are here',
And 'Fox, you've stolen all the geese',
Indulge in a musical triplet piece.
The harmony's location's been shifted,
Probably gone lower or been lifted.
To everyone's grief, it's no finer,
No one hits the F sharp minor.
Leitmotif in a Bruckner symphony;
Without the skill, it's a cacophony.
The most able soloist does fumble,
If the cello's notes are all in a jumble.

Vom wohltemperierten Klavier -[1]

The telescope's not in the orchestra section
But it's still an instrument in your collection.
And like the instruments we've seen,
It should be tuned, precise and clean.
To set sights upon is your exploitation,
Only to the correct calibration.
Here it really doesn't matter
If the crowd applauds, with a clatter,
If the thing explodes, that's elation,
Or it fails through bad computation.
And so you must crank up the handles,
Just as much as the violinist dandles.
He: with the perfect scale of fifths,
You: work out how far it is.
If you're wrong, all of the preparation
Is in vain, so's your target allocation.
But if you play without a care,
Even with music, to hell with you there!
Work it out for yourself, cos you won't always
find A tuner by the violinist's stand behind.
If you can do it, then it's good,
But even better if an expert would!

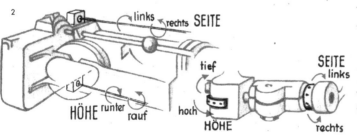

links rechts SEITE

tief

SEITE
links

HÖHE runter rauf   hoch

HÖHE

rechts

1. From The Well-Tempered Clavier..., 2. SEITE = Traverse, HÖHE = Elevation,
Links = left, Rechts = right, runter = lower, rauf = higher, hoch = up, tief = down.

zum wohljustierten Visier [1]

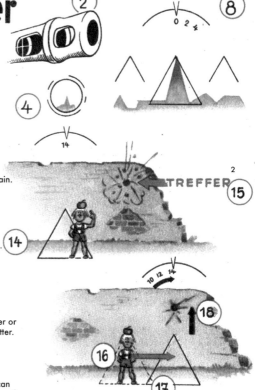

Calibration is not much different to twiddling with some bolts. If you can fix something, then you also can calibrate it.

Vibrations are poison for precision: long marches, hits on the turret, the first shots to hit a new vehicle. So this is what you have to do:

First we calibrate the graticule.
1. Place your vehicle on even ground, if possible
2. Stick a thin crosshair over the notch behind the muzzle brake.
3. Take the firing pin out and release the lock.
4. Fix the barrel via the crosshairs on something 2000 metres away, noting the spot on the terrain and leave it in this position.

Telescope: For this you will need a square-headed calibration tool.
5. Set the sighting gauge to '0', with a five-time magnification.
6. Take the protective cap off and apply the square-headed tool.
7. Adjust the main pointer according to the width and height of the same spot on the terrain.
8. Tighten everything back up.
9. Look through the sights again to make sure everything is correct.

Turret machine gun: You will also need the crosshair and duct tape here.
10. Stick the thin crosshair over the muzzle flash hider.
11. Disassemble the butt and safety catch, putting the top of the safety catch back in place.
12. Calibrate the machine gun according to the width and height of the same spot as before. Test it out with a quick shot. **If you can.**

Telescope: Look for a vertical wall at around 100 metres distance.
13. Adjust the estimated range so it is valid for anti-tank ammunition.
14. According to the rules, bring it around to a spot with good visibility.
15. Fire, and observe the impact closely.
16. Fix onto this **exact** spot and leave the barrel in this position.
17. Calibrate the main pointer in the sight only according **to the facing side** exactly, over or under the place of impact. (You have estimated the difference in elevation! This doesn't matter. The elevation has already been accurately calibrated with the crosshairs.)
18. Adjust the sights until the sighting point is at the elevation of the impact. Now you know the exact distance to the target (Keyword: Stain).

Turret machine gun: Here you do the same (but keep it 80 centimetres to the left) and can work with the same distance. Calibration is done, as you would expect, by the bolts underneath the machine gun bearing.

1...to the Well-Adjusted Sighting System, 2. Hit.

Die heilige Barbara [1]

Since the time of good Old Fritz,
St. Hubert was patron saint of hits.
The patron saint of tank guns now
Is St. Barbara without a doubt.
How to earn her protection:
Don't curse all signs of dejection.
But rather until the bitter end:
'St Barbara, please be my friend!'

The main purpose of your gun
Is that it can shoot at anyone,
And hopefully out front will fire
So as to not provoke her ire
Through a lack of loving care,
Else the gun'll point anywhere.
Look after the tank gun, KwK,
Oh, what a way it'll then spray.
You can't compare it to the rest
Because a), its range is the very
best, And b), wily, crafty shots
Will hit the most precise spots.
And c), the power in percussion
Is twice that of the Russian.
You'll shoot, when you look after
the hose, Towards then where the
enemy goes.

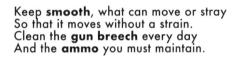

Sankt Hubert [2]

Keep **smooth**, what can move or stray
So that it moves without a strain.
Clean the **gun breech** every day
And the **ammo** you must maintain.

The gun belt and the bore,
De-oil them first before you fire.
Afterwards **oil more** than before
But only when the heat's expired.

Check the **connectors**, by and large,
And whether the **cables** are intact.
And if the **battery** has been charged;
It clearly pays to be exact.

The firing pins, check a fuse;
Check that everything's all right.
Notice what you can fix and use
Else you can't fire in the fight.

1. The holy Barbara, 2. Saint Hubert.

Don't travel without the **muzzle hood**,
Before you shoot, take off, unfestoon.
Unless iced up; can shoot through it
good, At the right time, not too soon.

Camo can indeed be foliage.
But from the muzzle clear it away
Before you shoot, **look for a smidge**
Of dirt inside, gone astray.

Remove at night (by torchlight)
Bits of ice, powder residue.
So when there's a gap in the fight,
A **hot barrel**, to **discharge** it through.

Sometimes you **miss** things by chance,
Something you can't always avoid.
So if your barrel has some **flatulence**,
Fire to one side so you don't destroy.

The **muzzle brake** itself recoils
About three quarters by the blow.
If it's too loose or overboils,
If this happens, don't fire the ammo.

The **recoil brake** adds another quarter on,
A kickback helped by lubrication.
If goo runs out of the hole upon,
If this happens, stop, fire cessation.

The **recuperator** brings back around
The barrel to the front again.
But if halfway or it breaks down,
If this happens, don't fire it then.

Recoil's measured by the **recoil gauge**,
Always push it forward, great.
If it says 'pause' and won't engage,
If this happens, don't fire, wait.

Gunner, this is all worthwhile
If you believe in all these rules.
Otherwise the gun, meanwhile,
Will then backfire on you fools.

1. Intermission, 2. Sardines.

Hand auf's Herz [1]

Note here what you must know best,
Place your hand upon your chest.
What you don't have in your head
Is on your fingertips instead.

Use middle finger to estimate
If the mantlet and barrel is straight.

Cock the machine gun and remove the muzzle flash
hider. The bolt mechanism must be easy to move with
your hand all the way and then must also spring back.

Falsch! [2]
This distance
shows that the
bolt is not locked.

[3] **Richtig!**
These two
edges must fit
together.

Your index finger shows point two
If the ammo feed's zippy too.

Feed a few cartridges through on the belt, let the
bolt snap through and go back.
The cartridges must be ejected.
Even better: test by firing.

Automatic fire with your thumb
Figure it out, even if you're dumb!

Pull the trigger. The bolt will draw and snap back.
This should happen as soon as the trigger is pulled,
immediately.

When the ring finger moves, at least,
It runs smoothly and is well-greased.

Remove the breech ring and the recoil spring. Move the bolt
mechanism very lightly with a clamping slide.

The little finger can be smart
See if the edge of the feeder is far apart

Snap the bolt through and lift off the cover. The front
face of the bolt housing must be trim with the edge of
the bottom belt feeder.

If memory of this doesn't linger,
Suck the wisdom from your fingers.

1. Hand on Heart. 2. Wrong 3. Right.

36

Liegt's an der Leitung?

First, check the warning lights
and keep them in good condition.

If both lights
are not on: 1, 2, 3, 4, 5

If the deflector is not
on: 6, 7, 8

If both are on, and you
haven't been hit: 9

If you can't find a fault, close all of the
contacts, ground the warning lights with
a pin on the bare wires and check the battery.

⑧ Push button is stuck, change the
emergency cable.

Unlock ⑦

Ⓐ ③

Ⓑ ⑤

Short circuit. Straighten out the firing points,
check the cables.

⑨ Clean the contacts, replace the studs,
replace the pins, clean the whole assembly.

④ Change the 15 amp
fuse.

⑥ Secure the Bosch jack.

If there is a defect with the slip ring
assembly, change the emergency
firing button.

Feuer

③

② Change the 40 amp
fuse.

① Turn on the main
switch.

1. How's the wiring?

Wir fahren nach Kurskreisel

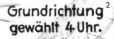

Grundrichtung[2] gewählt 4 Uhr.

2. So wird ausgerichtet:[3]

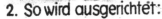

By mustering into position.

According to the start. All alignments and vehicles turn towards the 12 o'clock direction.

According to the compass at a distance of 20 metres.

Marschrichtung[4] somit Kurs 6 Uhr.

(1) Determine where you are.

(2) Align.

(3) Set the course on the dial standardised for a selected main course, for example, the 4 o'clock direction.

(4) Engage the device.

(5) Release

(6) Add in any orders to the dial, which the commanding officer has ordered after he has calculated if the manoeuvre will deviate from the main course.

Keeping on course: The two dials must show one number above the other. If the numbers stray to the right, turn it to the left, if they stray to the left, turn to the right.

New course: Change the order dial. If the number is smaller, turn it to the left. If the number is bigger, turn it to the right.

Stopping or turning off the tank:
1. Determine where you are.
2. Turn it off, otherwise you will drain the battery.

Before driving:
1. Engage the device.
2. Release, otherwise you will lose the information about the main course.

1. We make our way according to the Gyroscopic Course Line-up, 2. Main direction selected as the 4 o'clock direction, 3. Orientate:, 4. Direction of manoeuvre on this course at 6 o'clock.

You can hear many radio bands
From all over many different lands.
And you believe what does transpire,
Heard from coil, valve and wire.
And say, 'If I don't want to be deceived,
I question all the noise received!'
Great was the rage in appearance,
The doubters thought it was interference.
'Twas however the tones pristine
From Weber's 'Marksman' ('Wolf's Glen' scene).
Now sharply divide on your receiver,
The short wave from the long by a lever.
In modern times the radio,
Strange new options it does bestow...

...for the new on board communication system will fulfill all of your desires!!

1. With a button, the commander 'chooses' the three-way microphone when he wants to speak.

2. As the Wireless operator, you are responsible for commander's main concerns of communication on board.
You operate, along with the driver or the commander, two receivers; you can listen to both separately.

3. And the last one of your dreams can now come true:
The gunner can also take part in radio communication!

1. Wireless.

Hier Vermittlung Panther

Wireless and intercom 1
Wireless 2
On / Off 3
Wireless Operator's microphone 4
Wireless Operator's Headset 5
Connect 6
Break 7

FUNK 2

FUNK u. BORD 1

FUNK 2

Ein • Aus 3

FUNKER-MIKROFON 4

FUNKER-FERNHÖRER 5

KOPPLUNG 6

TRENNUNG 7

KOPPLUNG 3

The on board communication box is the small switchboard for the communication system. It is looked after by the wireless operator.

The next page shows the different toggle switch options of the communication system in connection with the wireless communication to those outside of the tank.

The position of the controls on the communication box, shown on the right, are called 'Connect' and 'Break'.

With telephones there is the exchange;
Radiating out, all arranged.
A connection using many leads;
As go-betweens, lovely girls indeed.
And because of field conditions
In the Panther, they can't be in position.
But because it plays the same role,
The **communication box** is in control.

1. You're through to the Panther telephone exchange, 2. Wireless, 3. Connect.

~Die~ Grundstellung [1]

Funk

FB — F

K — T

Kopplung

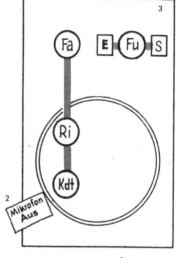

First thing, what the new recruit,
Barely clothed, must do astute:
He must learn to stand up straight,
Long known this would be his fate.
This task is the 'basic position'
And with soldiers, a recognition
This has been a duty for many years,
If you speak to your superiors.
And what concerns the new cadets
Is also practised with your radio sets:
A basic position's also needed here,
Look at it now and it'll be clear.

The basic position of the on board communication system **in battle is 'Wireless'** Who hears who?

Who hears who?

Look at this drawing of the crew!

1. **Wireless Operator:** You alone can hear your receiver and can transmit!
2. You are switched off from the rest of your crew.
3. **Commander, Gunner** and **Driver** can speak with each other.

Intercommunication under radio silence:
Receiver and transmitter off -, communication box turned on, in the position 'Wireless - Intercom'.
Do not forget to adjust the volume on the communication box!

1. The basic position, 2. Microphone off, 3. Fa=Fahrer (Driver); Ri=Richtschütze (Gunner); Kdt=Kommandant (Commander);
Fu=Funker (Wireless Operator); E=Empfangen (receive); S=Senden (transmit).

~~~ **Kommandant**

. . . is transmitting

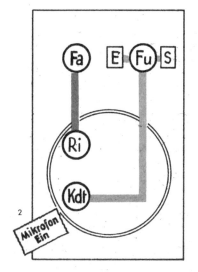

Any number can be used
On the telephone, free to choose.
And for the commander, this is the case;
A microphone in front of his face.
On his head it is connected,
Importantly where he would expect it.
This advantage he must use it,
Calmly without being too confusing...

...he pushes the button to transmit on his microphone to 'On' and connects to the Wireless Operator.

Who hears what?

1. **Wireless Operator** and **Commander** hear radio communication from outside of the tank.
2. **Gunner** and **Driver** can speak to each other without disturbing you or the commander.
3. Wireless Operator! Upon the order 'Wireless Operator transmit!', you push the button for the tone and switch to 'Telephone'. Now the commander can also transmit.

Funk

Kopplung

1. Commander, 2. Microphone on.

42

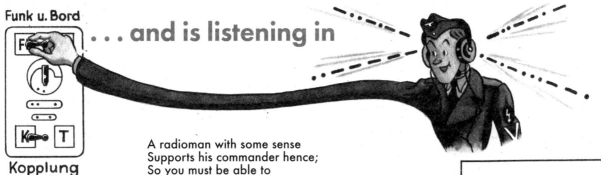

Funk u. Bord

Kopplung

... and is listening in

A radioman with some sense
Supports his commander hence;
So you must be able to
Save him a job to do.
Don't get on his nerves fragmental,
Pestering him with the incidentals.
And present to him in chatter
Only the most important matters.
In this case you **must** perturb,
He must hear of your blurb.
And anything that is required,
Switch to 'Wireless and intercom' wired.

If there is an important radio conversation, the Wireless Operator will turn on to 'Wireless and intercom'.

All can hear

Commander, gunner and driver. Everyone will hear when he breaks in.

Wireless operator! When you switch over you will hear a response from your commander; then don't interrupt and turn back to 'wireless'. You can then only hear the important conversations; note them down exactly so that you can repeat them afterwards.

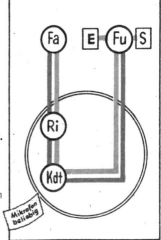

1. Any Microphone.

Zuviel auf einmal[1]

An office worker with lots to do
On the surface is pushing through
Taking down so many dictations
And heaps of telephone conversations
He is kept upon his toes
With telephones, an acrobatic pose.
But does end this cosy feeling
When every phone there is squealing.

The Company Commander (the boss) has 2 receivers in his Panther:
One is a connection with the battalion and the other is to the radio with the Company. Both receivers are linked.
Wireless traffic can come across both receivers, Then the Wireless Operator turns switch onto 'Disconnect'.
The basic setting for the radio communication box with the commander is '

WIRELESS - INTERCOM'

Who hears what?

1. **Wireless Operator!** You hear Receiver 2.
2. The **Commander** hears Receiver 1.
3. **Gunner** and **Driver** hear, together with the **Commander**, Receiver 1.

Although the receivers are separated, everyone can hear everyone on board!

Funk u. Bord

Trennung

1. Too much all at once, 2. Any microphone, 3. Panzerführer.

Verwicklungen[1]

He who doesn't keep the wires neat
Will look like Laocoön living on the street.
And he gets entangled in a crowd
'Cause there are so many wires about.
And for radio this is defined:
A tidy house, a tidy mind!
Note the main point of that line:
Everything has its own place assigned.
And from these cable wire knot tethers,
The expert doesn't seem very clever.
You're more likely to get interference;
Nothing's worse than incoherence
What you don't need, without delay,
To its own place, cleared away.
So cable lengths unnecessarily,
Not hanging unused arbitrarily.
Pack away what's not required,
Make sure you don't trample on the wires.
Don't pull the leads out from the jacks.
Else it breaks off all the contacts!
Although you're wireless, wire your brain
So everything's tidy and maintained.

Your company has, to add at last,
Two frequencies in which to broadcast.
Have some rest, then have some stress,
Otherwise you'll miss success.
Whoever lets themselves have rest,
Can snap into it safely, quick and best.
First have some rest, then the action,
Otherwise you'll find you've this distraction:
Suddenly, seized up, in a flummox
Just sat there with your radio box.

Don't make spaghetti with your cables during radio operations:
Pick your microphone up first, then your headphones!

Next to you on the right, in Box Z 23, are 40 amp **fuses**, which protect your equipment. If you use the equipment too forcefully or short-circuit it, don't be surprised if the receiver or the transmitter blow out. If the fuses are out or have failed, you will have no current. Check them, first at the master switch for the battery and the main fuse underneath the commander's seat.

1. Entanglements.

3 Tasttonellis
Frequenz-Equilibristik

On the radio there's a concert,
There it is, if you stay alert.
Press the button down secure
Until the reception's clear and pure.
This is not just for a radio show
But by radio operations, it is so.
Main wireless station gives a sign,
All receivers are aligned.
Secondly, with some little tricks,
The receiver is aligned and fixed
With the receiver, on the nose!
Why do we do it? So it goes:
A juggler elegantly negotiates
The force of gravity and its weight.
The man, a sin he demonstrates
With his blonde female team-mate.

She throws to him without a break
One ring and another for him to take
In his hands that they are caught
With success, no second thoughts.
Thrown too far or thrown too high
You can wave this trick goodbye.
The ring flies off into the air,
It's not able to be ensnared.
With the radio, without the rings
It's pretty much the same thing.
If frequency is wrong like the height,
Radio traffic is in a plight.
Transmitters send to open space
If not aligned in the right place.
So, the short waves and the long,
No one gets them as they go along.
The commander can't hear communication,
If the transmitter isn't in calibration.

All transmitters in a company must be on exactly the same wavelength. Transmitters that are not calibrated to this, will not be heard.

1. The 3 Buttonellis Frequency Equilibristics.

Abgleichen! [1] what does . . .

the main wireless station do?

Send call signs or telegraphy on the designated wavelength. On this wavelength, which has been broadcast, the main wireless station and all other transmitters are now equalised.

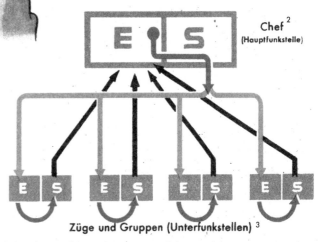

Chef [2]
(Hauptfunkstelle)

Züge und Gruppen (Unterfunkstellen) [3]

the supporting wireless station do?

1. Turn the tuning knob to '0' and the volume control to the left.
2. Tune in to the main wireless station on the receiver with the loudest volume. But be accurate!
3. Pull out the antenna and the connecting cable from the transmitter and the receiver.
4. Adjust the wavelength of your transmitter using the button until you hear the tone in the receiver at a good volume. But be accurate!

When you have done this, all transmitters will be working on the same wavelength!

1. Equalising!, 2. R-T Company Commander (the boss) (Main wireless station), 3. Squadrons and Troops (Supporting wireless stations).

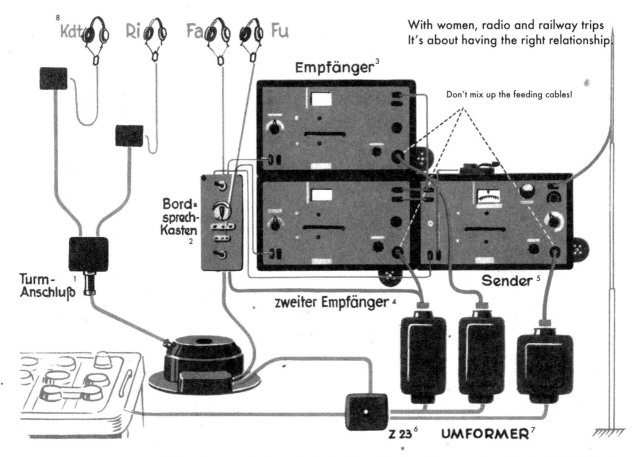

Kdt Ri Fa Fu

Empfänger³

Bord=
sprech-
Kasten
²

Turm-
Anschluß¹

zweiter Empfänger⁴

Sender⁵

Z 23⁶ UMFORMER⁷

With women, radio and railway trips
It's about having the right relationship.

Don't mix up the feeding cables!

1. Connection to turret, 2. Communication Switch box, 3. Receiver, 4. Second receiver, 5. Sender, 6. Z 23, 7. Transformer,
8. Kdt=Kommandant (Commander); Ri=Richtschütze (Gunner); Fa=Fahrer (Driver); Fu=Funker (Wireless Operator).

Entstörung [1]

Certainly a household full of renters
Is an electrical epicentre.
You'll easily get some interference
From your 12-tubes; incoherence.
Crackling from dusk 'till dawn
Appliance jammed-up, all forlorn.
Not just at home is your radio
Like this, in the Panther also.
In the earpiece, crackles with static
Radioman grabs it, with rage phlegmatic
The cables are, in all of these cases,
Back to where the interference traces.
The wires are all frazzled and frayed,
It's recommended, they're replaced, remade.
If the caps aren't sealed up tight
This de-jamming won't work right!

Before everything else, tighten up both of the interference suppression caps well. The Panther is good at eliminating interference if the whole electrical system is working faultlessly. Also, think particularly of and about the electrode gap of the lights and the cable connections and the magneto. Connect all 25 cm of the tightly-laid, shielded cable with a metal clamp with a gauge!

Anything that crackles in rhythm with the running motor and promptly stops when the vehicle is in storage means that the cause is the ignition. If the crackling gradually stops, then it is the alternator. If you suspect there is a problem with a switch, the radiator fan or the heading indicator, you can find the troublemaker by turning things on and off as there may be loose connections from moving along.

Radio mechanic: **When removing and replacing the engine or the transmission gear and lifting the turret, you must disconnect and connect all of the wires!**

1. Tuning.

Selbst Verhör![1]

FF
LLL

The more mechanisation advances, the less mechanised is the soul.

Fuller

The strongest tank isn't worth its weight
If the driver can't drive straight.
Penetrating power's all up the spout
If the tank can't move about.
Radio operator sends out to empty space
If the driver's useless in place.
But just the man, we here have,
Someone you can all dream of:
Perfect example, Paul Gearstick's his name
This was his claim to fame.
Firstly he's a fine serviceman,
Secondly, a comrade, a good kinsman.
And from all these, he does know
That everyone does his duty though.
He is not pedantic in precision
But keeps his kit in good condition.
He's not a one-upper know-it-all
But knows he knows enough to call
On his elders or seniors to accrue
Things he can learn anew.
He's no philosopher, but his trick
Is knowing he's not stubborn or thick.
If there's something new, he never fails
To ask about all the details.

In short, he isn't bloody-minded too,
With no posturing silly to-do.
His best feature, it is thus;
He's conscientious and scrupulous.
He fights happy and for good reasons
Against his own inner demons.
With which the following **5 questions**
To see if he can, in suggestion.
Before climbing in to his machine,
He makes sure everything is pristine.
He doesn't need to vex his brain,
He can count on five fingers again:
Of the two 'Fs' think of first
Fill and **Filter,** are rehearsed.
When filling, please think of this rule:
Check oil and water and the fuel.
The full five, it's quick so far
Think of 3 big capital 'Rs'
The 3 Rs, you must utter:
The **Rounds,** the **Running gear,** and the **Rudder!**
When Paul does count on his fingers
You know no fault with the Panther lingers!
Do what Paul does, examine it,
And so prevail your best bits!

FILL – FILTER – ROUNDS – RUNNING GEAR – RUDDER

1. Self-Examination.

Refuelling

The tank burns if, it's clear to all,
Naps next to the tank does Gearstick Paul!
You'll have a longer life in view
If you don't pour fuel next to you.
Wash it off and make sure
You can go to work secure.
Petrol is with lead combined;
Damages skin and can make you blind!

730 liter

150 km Straße oder [1]

100 km Gelände

Refuelling is an art!

Check beforehand whether the canister really is for petrol engines (in winter it is yellow petrol for the Eastern Front) - and not diesel. Then make sure that the funnel is clean. Secure the filter within. Pour in carefully, especially if the exhaust pipes are hot! If it is windy, place yourself in the wind, and if it is raining or snowing, lean yourself over the filling hole.

What can make proper refuelling easier, if the petrol, due to leaky hoses, connectors and fuel pumps, drips away? Check here again!

Drain petrol and deposited dirt out of the fuel tanks and through the floor of the hull.
Do not start up the engine if petrol or oil is in the hull!

1. 150 km by road or 100 km over land.

Kanisterging[1]

Listen now, hear the adventure
Of the hideous Jerry Can Vulture!
He is a greedy so-and-so,
His claws steal like a sibling though.
He steals cans and pumps and drums;
The more outrageous, the better it comes.
The Home Front toils monstrously
But not for this vulture so beastly!

Here the vulture's picked up the scent,
There's sumptuous feeding in intent.
The most beautiful things are then thrown
By the ton towards his beak alone!

Here lie cables, tools and a winch,
All there for the vulture to pinch.
He'll damage all supplies we need,
Just so this bird of prey can feed!

Every drop of fuel in battle
is worth as much as a drop
of blood!
Clemenceau

See here Paul Gearstick being a wastrel,
Again, the upper hand has this kestrel.
Paul's helping out, all is prepared,
In his salon, is everything there:
From his bath to natural soothing light,
This fat cat wants for nothing, right?
His self-invented heating ends
The frost on which happiness depends.
But a stove is worth its weight in gold,
But not if it's his to behold.

Hide your drums and jerry cans
From this beast, you'll understand!
Only he who has ideas unsound
Would throw these drums into the ground.
After fueling, pick up every bit,
If something's missing, go back for it!

1. The Jerry Can Vulture.

52

This is the start and the finish. The sixteenth round has begun. Lead driver Manfred von Brauchitsch has just entered the pits for refuelling and new tyres. The mechanics work feverishly because his fellow competitor is also in the pits for spare parts. Who finishes first? Brauchitsch? Amid the roar of the crowd, the engine starts up, there - a spark at the back - **the car is on fire!!!** Race organiser, Neubauer, pulls Manfred straight out of the cockpit, as the fire extinguishers spray...

How did this happen? 25 litres of petrol can be pumped into the fuel tank in 1 second. The mechanic turned the tap only a split-second too late and 10 litres ran over the hot exhaust...

Petrol can do things terrific,
Flows where it wants, it's prolific.
Unloads its power so suddenly
Up high with a bang, you'll see.
What good is a tank exploded?
Much better in one piece and loaded.

Your Panther will blow up
If the hull is silted up.
In this case, disintegration
In bits, smoke, bang, immolation!

1. Attention, attention... the German Grand Prix at the Nürburgring!

How pumps were in times past,
A fire extinguisher was so vast:
Four men it took, with some sweat,
On each side, to spray beget.
After a breather and some rest,
A meagre spray is expressed.
A sturdy chief with a gut
Controls spray, hose and water butt.
Finally, success was in the net,
At least the ashes are now wet.
In the past, how it was instead,
Schiller's clock can be read.
Nowadays it's not benighted
If a Panther's been ignited:
A fire now can't break out,
A detector you're never without.

Switch off the fans and the petrol nozzle!

When water is not flowing, quickly take off the locking cap, **1**, and forcefully press the button down, **2**. Pressing 5 times will give you 7 seconds of water flow. You'll get 8 seconds if pressured and the container is full, 4 seconds when empty.

Keep the fuse, **3**, in working order (15 amps), otherwise the heat detector won't work.
Don't clamp onto the pipes, **4**, otherwise they'll wear through and the extinguisher will spray uselessly.

The extinguishing material is a mix of carbon, chlorine and bromine, used in emergencies as 'Tetra' liquid.

1. The Fire Brigade.

Deine Vergaser[1]

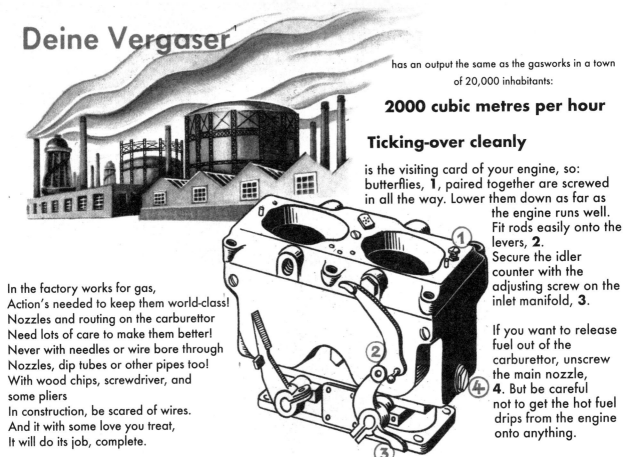

has an output the same as the gasworks in a town of 20,000 inhabitants:

2000 cubic metres per hour

Ticking-over cleanly

is the visiting card of your engine, so: butterflies, **1**, paired together are screwed in all the way. Lower them down as far as the engine runs well. Fit rods easily onto the levers, **2**. Secure the idler counter with the adjusting screw on the inlet manifold, **3**.

If you want to release fuel out of the carburettor, unscrew the main nozzle, **4**. But be careful not to get the hot fuel drips from the engine onto anything.

In the factory works for gas,
Action's needed to keep them world-class!
Nozzles and routing on the carburettor
Need lots of care to make them better!
Never with needles or wire bore through
Nozzles, dip tubes or other pipes too!
With wood chips, screwdriver, and some pliers
In construction, be scared of wires.
And it with some love you treat,
It will do its job, complete.

1. Your carburettors.

On the street, say hellos and goodbyes,
Here you notice the **engine jet size.**

'Six five' is called the pilot jet,
Knows every Panther kid as yet.
And firstly it is named,
Two, three, five, brake 150, proclaimed.
The second is screwed in tight
200, brake, two, two five, right!

When the carburettor is dismantled, pay attention
to **the** following:

The seals are faultless and the throttle valve
closes tightly.

The float gauge is not dented and the bearings
turn iso run.

The choke tube is inserted so that you can read
38 or 40.

The intermediate ring is lying correctly on the
choke tube (the central choke tube should be
sitting neither too high or too deep).

The carburettor pilot jet, particularly the hole
on the side, and similar channels should be clear.

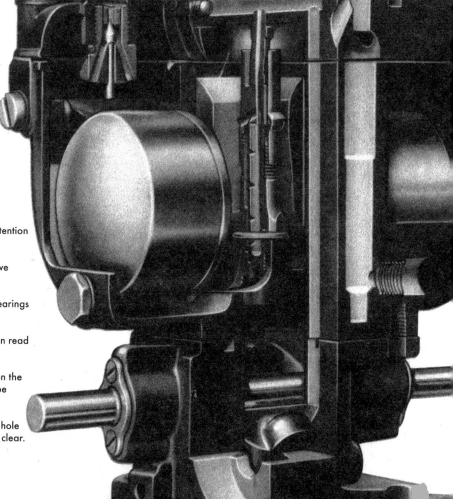

The battery

...on an electric cart
Are there so it runs on the rails and starts.
You hear at the railway this type of sound,
You will know you're holiday-bound.
The wagon accumulates all suitcases,
Packets, boxes, and prams to places.
And it does its job here just as good
As it on the Panther should:
It gives light, air, puts out and starts,
Tank shoots if you maintain the parts.
And this you must comprehend
Otherwise you'll be at a loose end.
You'll be under the lantern waiting
Like Lili Marleen, so captivating!

So take note:
1. Battery: wet, full of dust and dirt,
   Clean it before you use it first!
2. If connections do not befit,
   You're apt to get a short circuit.
3. Don't leave on the battery switch,
   If you do, drop dead in a ditch!
4. If you see someone with a match
   And acid level's just right in its batch;
   It's much better to be kind,
   And look after those left behind.
5. Battery likes it at month's end,
   If you're gentle, and to it attend.

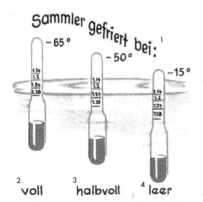

1. The battery freezes at, 2. Full, 3. Half-full, 4. Empty.

Hold the earthing of the negative lead of the battery when it is clean and lightly grease it. Remove oxide build-up with a caustic solution, not with a brush. By doing this, you will prevent any rotten breakdowns.
Tighten the vent plugs and keep their vents free, otherwise the cell cover will burst. Do not disconnect the battery when it is empty, instead charge and discharge it every month (particularly in the winter when you've topped up the acid levels!).
The battery must be tightly fixed in place in the Panther!

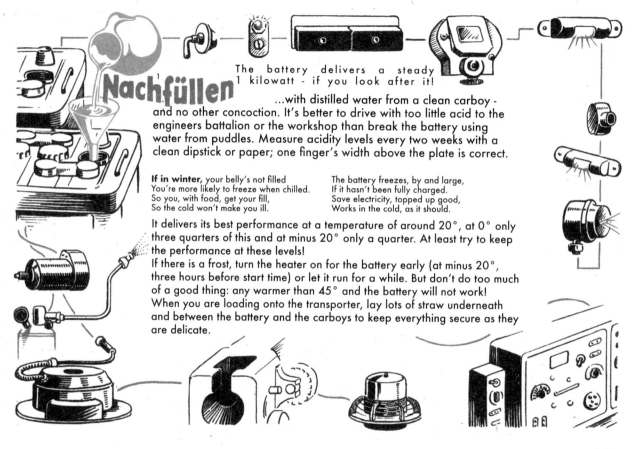

Nachfüllen [1]

The battery delivers a steady 1 kilowatt - if you look after it!

...with distilled water from a clean carboy - and no other concoction. It's better to drive with too little acid to the engineers battalion or the workshop than break the battery using water from puddles. Measure acidity levels every two weeks with a clean dipstick or paper; one finger's width above the plate is correct.

If in winter, your belly's not filled
You're more likely to freeze when chilled.
So you, with food, get your fill,
So the cold won't make you ill.

The battery freezes, by and large,
If it hasn't been fully charged.
Save electricity, topped up good,
Works in the cold, as it should.

It delivers its best performance at a temperature of around 20°, at 0° only three quarters of this and at minus 20° only a quarter. At least try to keep the performance at these levels!

If there is a frost, turn the heater on for the battery early (at minus 20°, three hours before start time) or let it run for a while. But don't do too much of a good thing: any warmer than 45° and the battery will not work!

When you are loading onto the transporter, lay lots of straw underneath and between the battery and the carboys to keep everything secure as they are delicate.

1. Top-up.

A cigar, cigarette or pipe
Can't do much without a light.
Lighter's as good as a match,
Useless if not up to scratch.
Flint is wet, the wick has rust,
So look after it you must.
And if you do your duty rarely,
When you need it, it won't play fairly!

A girl, to you, is very attractive,
When she's tanned, young and active!
With the spark plugs this is true,
They must be brown, it's right for you.

right

The Lighter

Spark plugs get their face so great,
When you drive, but not in idling state.
So should it be with girls thereof;
She's made beautiful through love.

Spark plugs need some love likewise,
Hold them in your heart and eyes.
Your engine will kick the bucket
When with rust and oil mucky.
But don't clean it using a knife,
A brush is a better way of life!

Bending and...

Too big or too small, a mishap,
Often is the electrode gap.
Can be through pressure or some bending,
Keep it in order, flawlessly attending.
If you don't do this good and well,
An expert will do it and excel!
If you don't do what we've discussed,
The spark plugs will all go to rust.

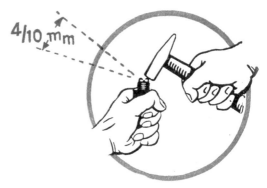

4/10 mm

carbonized

With pimples, blemishes and some spots,
For you, no one will have the hots.
First impressions, usually duff,
And on your spark plugs, not good enough:
With this rusty, dirty face,
Engine goes bang, a disgrace.

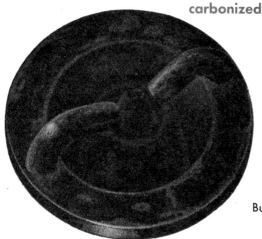

If the engine is left running for some time, the gap between the electrodes will become too large as they burn off. Too small a gap and the ignition spark will be too weak. Be precise when fitting the 4/10 mm spark plug gauge. **Bend** the grounded electrode with a hammer or screwdriver to fit, but without damaging the central electrode and the insulator!

But don't make too much of a habit of bending the electrodes, instead:
Rejuvenate the engine with new spark plugs!

60

...Breaking

In illnesses there is inflammation;
In engines, burning up's damnation.
This should not you affect,
If you choose spark plugs correct.
With the Panther it's contrived,
To choose W 2 5 5!
Wrong one in due to your toil,
The spark plug's
fouled up in oil.

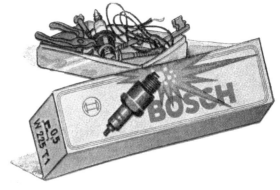

Oiled up

Oily skin and complexion
Doesn't receive much affection.
Oil and sweat's not prepossessing,
Clean peachy tones are a blessing.
An oily sheen's too unattractive
For sparks of love to now be active.
If plugs are oily with clogged parts,
Engine won't be able to start!

Carry well-packaged spare spark plugs with you!
Before screwing them in, check the front of the spark plugs and
the electrodes! Then turn them gently threaded with the suppressor
cap and tighten them up normally with the spark plug spanner.
But be careful and **don't break the insulator!**

For girls without any inner cheer
Champagne doesn't help, it's too dear.
The best petrol-air mixture of all
Goes unnoticed by the board.
So it's not too big, it's compressed;
The spark ignites it in process.
Paul Gearstick fails in ignominy,
The spark plugs here look too skinny.

Lean

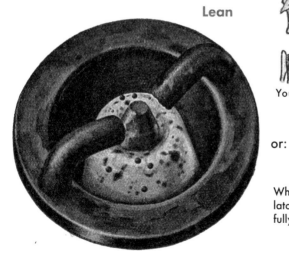

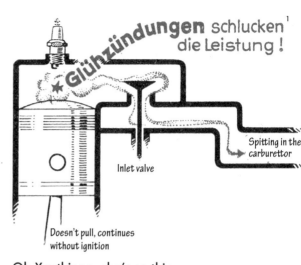

Glühzündungen schlucken die Leistung![1]

Inlet valve

Spitting in the carburettor

Doesn't pull, continues without ignition

Oh Xanthippe, she's so thin,
You'll stab yourself on her chin.

You've given the engine too little of the mixture it needs.

or:
- given it too much pre-ignition (5° over dead-centre is fine).
- you've been driving with too much speed.
- you've driven with cooling fans turned off and ventilating louvres closed.
- your thermostat is switched off.

What is wrong with the spark plugs? Unscrew all of them: perhaps the insulator body or the packing rings are broken? Reinstall the spark plugs carefully, swapping out old ones for new ones, and tighten them up well!

1. Ignition detonations/mis-fires reduce power.

62

Friction

After a cold dip, here look around,
A lady's getting herself rubbed down
From bathing, shivering from cold,
This friction's working well, all told.
For she is warming up her limbs,
Reviving herself after the swim.
Although this warmth is so splendid,
Too much rubbing's not recommended.
It can lead to incineration,
All that helps is **lubrication...**

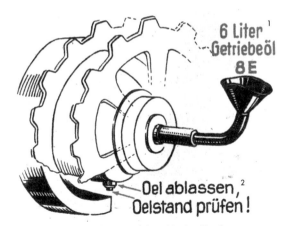

6 Liter [1]
Getriebeöl
8 E

← Oel ablassen, [2]
Oelstand prüfen !

1. 6 litres of gearbox oil 8E, 2. Oil drain/check oil level.

...and checking the **oil level:**
For the engine, the fan drive and the gearbox, take readings with a **dipstick.** While starting up (idling!) wipe the dipstick with a clean cloth and dip it in: The oil should show neither under the lowest mark nor above the highest mark.
When **checking the bolts,** check across on the right from the clutch spigot (using the 19 spanner), on the turret drive check across on the left between the oil pressure pump (14 spanner) and under the final drive (32 spanner); if oil comes out when you unscrew the bolts, you have enough in there.
In the **winter,** top up the engine with the army-issue winter oil. Should it get colder than minus 30°, pour in a mixture of 20 litres of winter oil and 6 litres of petrol. But then check the oil levels more often and fill up when the engine is warm, because the petrol evaporates while driving (after 3 hours).

Schmierung[1]

With tanks and rationing frustration
Is a problem of lubrication!
There will be enough lard,
If you sparingly safeguard.
Really awful greedy cops
Lubricate their sarnie doorstops!
Whoever's too lazy to economise,
Will find out next day to their demise.
So by the next day unfulfilling
Have empty hand as a sandwich filling.
The Panther is not quite so greedy
Lubricate it when it needs it!

Pour in	where	with		what
Engine	red bolt on the left	27 mm spanner	26 litres	
Fan drive	two filler necks	27 per	1¾ litres	**engine oil**
Hydraulic gear (with sieve!)	filler neck, on the right	17 per	4 litres	
Gearbox	2 in the gearbox housing	22 mm spanner	21 litres	
	1 in the oil container	27	12 litres	**transmission oil 8E**
	3 in the clutch spigot	17	¼ litre	
	in the gearbox oil cooler	22	15 litres	
Turret drive	between the oil pressure pumps	22	3 litres	
Oil pressure system (with sieve!)	in the oil container	19 per	7 litres	**shock absorber oil (purple)**
	Vibration damper filler cap on the side	22 per	1¾ litres	

1. Lubrication.

Changing the oil in the ## Gearbox

...when it is warm.

1. Undo the drain plugs on the gearbox housing, **4**, the oil container (tool 27) on the clutch spigot (tool 19), **6**.
1. Disassemble the edge filter, clean it (but don't take it apart) and scrape out the oil residue (tool 27), **8**.
2. Let the engine idle for a short while, so that the channels are emptied.
3. Put the drain plugs and the edge filter back on. With sealing rings! Fill with new oil.
4. Check the oil level! In the winter, switch off the gearbox oil cooler with the square headed spanner on the three-headed stopcock (with the line vertical).

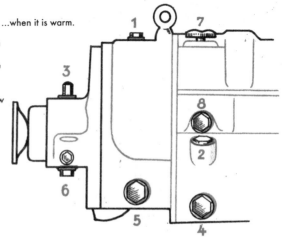

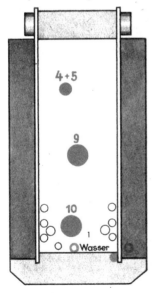

Well known it was for its huge size,
Did the cask from Heidelberg comprise.
Under which spent many for many an hour,
Laying under the tap in a shower.
It changed over time and in many ways,
Like your hull floor always.
The old oil, instead of from the vines,
Oh, what a life so fine!

Draining the engine...
when it is warm and the ignition key is pulled out.

Unscrew the oil sump and oil container (tool 17), **10**. If the oil has run out, turn the engine over. Don't forget to clean the oil filter at this point!

Tighten up the drain plugs. With the seals! Fill up with new oil. Tighten up the screws well, otherwise everything will come out. Is the oil level correct in the engine?

...and the turret drive
Undo the drain plugs (tool 22) and do the same thing with the hull floor (tool 19), **9.**

1. Water, 2.1896 Leitungs Heimer (tap water).

Die FILTERWÄSCHE

Here, with lovely pink outfits,
The unruly summer wind plays,
But I make no bones about it,
That all of this, I can praise.
With fresh clothes; scent and sheen,
You feel free as you wander,
Your filter also wants to be clean,
Something else you should launder!
If left in dirt and residue,
Changing the oil, it's no use,
In this case it's best for you,
Leave in the old mucky juice.

If the barrel is not clean, what you
pour in will go sour.   Horace

Air filter

Unscrew the wing nuts. Pull out the filter. Take off the sheet
metal cover and the filter element. Pour the oil away, wash
everything out and dry.

Pour in 1½ litres of old engine oil up to the mark shown on
the filter housing (in winter, mix with ¾ litre of diesel).
Re-assemble the filter; don't crimp the seals against the
intake pipe when you're screwing them on.
Check the wing nuts regularly and tighten them!
Don't trample around on the filters!

1. Washing your filter.

Oil filter

Set the turret at 4 o'clock and open the right hatch in the bulkhead. Loosen the cover (tool 14). When lifting it off, make sure you don't lose the compression spring!

Drain the filter element well, then take the whole thing out.

Undo the wing nuts underneath, remove the washers.

Wash out and dry everything, particularly the fabric disc and the filter housing.

First put in the filter disc, then alternate fitting the outer anchorage plate and the filter disc into the slits on the tube. The holes on the inner edge of the anchorage plate must match up with the wing nuts. Put the end on and tighten the wing nuts until you feel some resistance. Now the filter element should be secure; if the discs are loose, then you've forgotten to do something. Every disc and every compression spring must be there, otherwise the filter won't work!

Put the element back in its housing, with the cover on, tighten the 3 bolts to the same tension and check the pipeline to the engine!

Fuel filter

Set the turret at 2 o'clock, open the left hatch on the bulkhead and unscrew the filter (tool 17). Take it out into the fighting compartment, lift off the cover (tool 10) and wash the element and housing out; but don't use water! Screw the filter element and the cover back on well!

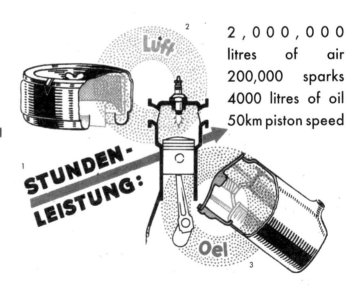

2,000,000 litres of air
200,000 sparks
4000 litres of oil
50km piston speed

1. Hourly output, 2. Air, 3. Oil.

Fetten [1]

Boots were brittle, frail and fragile,
The leather isn't very agile.
And the care of the shoes
Was carried out with grease and ooze.
For your car to keep you on the move,
Grease it regularly to improve.
Panther'll appreciate your effort,
More than likely won't forget it!

To discover something, very many - perhaps most
people, must first know that it is there already.
Georg Christoph Lichtenberg

First wipe the nipple clean and then press down until the excess grease collar appears. Mix the grease in the winter with half engine oil, when it is really cold, mix it with frost-proof petrol.

Grease the clutch **thrust bearing in the main clutch**. Take the sheet metal covering off and step on the clutch. Drip some oil onto the 3 shiny bolts.

Before greasing the **road wheels**, first take off the locking screw on the hatch cover (tool 12) and remove the nipple joints (tool 17).

When you get an opportunity, also regularly grease the joins and bolts on the hatch cover and engine cover, otherwise they will rust solid.

You need in the joints lubrication,
And in the filter corrugations.
Circle 1 The **filter** operates,
Providing that you grease the plates.
By the engine, at the back, affixed
Note the number of the nipple: 6!

If your nutrition is very strong,
Power flows into your limbs along.
Circle 2 **Power's taken up**,
Providing you've fat in your gut.
In the centre, Panther's greased great
Enough with nipple 48!

For power to increase in size,
It's recommended to economise.
Circle 3 Here **power's guided**
As long as grease is provided.
Nipple's hard to see, now and then,
So note the number well, it's 10!

With negligence of your feet,
On the march you'll suffer every beat.
No. 4 Boots are **lightly padded**
Provided that grease is added.
Grease them up and clean them well,
Note left and right: a dozen, twelve!

1. Grease.

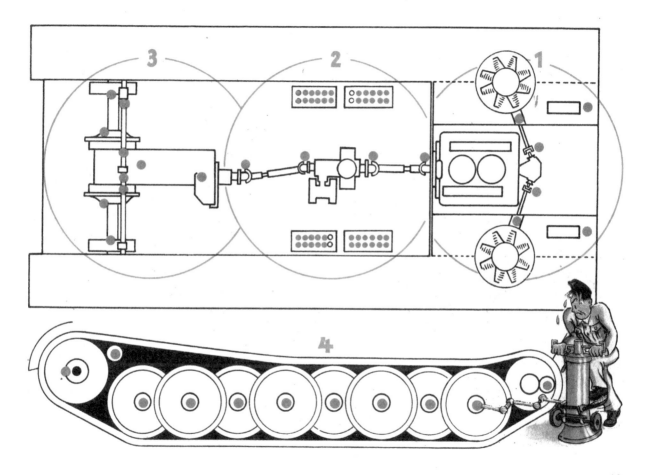

Water

No girl would bad temper spout,
From vermicelli and sauerkraut.
When champagne in the glass does fizz,
The vital spirit's woken as it is.
And on ice the champagne's put,
It goes cold, but the girl gets hot.
If you don't cool it, you'll behold,
The champagne's warm, the girl goes cold!
Bit of cool bubbly, in the blood raring,
She's in the mood, he gets daring.
But warm champagne brings no feeling,
So see, how important is the cooling!

So to your thirst you must cater,
First fill up your **radiator!**

This is how water circulates in the engine

Fill

...but slowly!

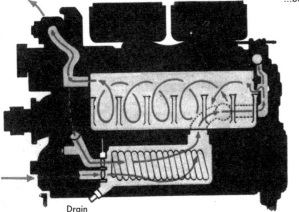

After use, leave the engine running slowly and then turn it off again. You can definitely re-fill it with 30 to 40 litres. Undo the locking cap and don't block up the thread (plastic!)

Drain off...   using the open filler cap

and make sure the thermostat is 'on'! You only need to undo the drain cock left on the hull floor (tool 36). Then turn the engine over so that it all drains out.
Never start it up without water!

When tubes and pipes and seals are tight,
Coolant flows - nothing else in sight!

Drain

70

Wind

The ancient Egyptian pharaohs
Often sweated on their thrones.
So stood around in their rooms
Were slaves holding palm leaf plumes.
And so they wagged with the fronds,
Obedient to the illustrious bonce.
Today one can get a cooling
With something a lot less gruelling.
No one has, like way back when,
In your house so many men.
When heat reigns like the Equator,
Instead whirrs the ventilator.

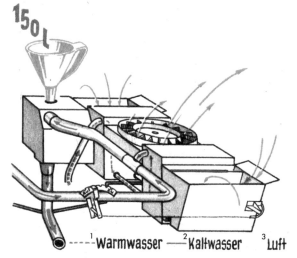

1. Warm water, 2. Cold water, 3. Air.

Obstruct the bars on the air intake,
Is for your Panther a mistake.
He will get in return
Heat stroke or a bad sunburn!

The fan keeps the fighting compartment cosily warm.
The gunner only has to pull the lever on the bulkhead and
warm air will be blown in. You regulate the **coolant iso
cooling water temperature** with the heating in the
fighting compartment and the fan valves; **it should not
go above 90°!**

If it is too hot outside, release the lever switch for the fan
gear unit under the left magneto (tool 14) when the engine is
stopped: screw it down tight onto 'increases cooling'.
Then turn up the fan.

It's freezing . . .

Only those of tough constitution
Can tolerate such ablutions.
Anyone else's life's cut short,
By this harsh winter sport.
It's not just you that's ill at ease,
In winter, water will also freeze.
So freezes, in even the warmest frock,
The water in your engine block!
To make it tougher, problem fixed,
With anti-freeze in the mix.
Else after a while, from the frost,
Important bits will be lost!

This is how you warm up the cooling water!

1. You must be satisfied that the heating pipe is clean, otherwise there'll be fire works when you use the blow torch! Also clean the gauze strainer! Turn off the thermostat.
2. Before heating, every crewman must be out of the Panther! Close hatches and turn off the fighting compartment heating: carbon dioxide hazard!
3. Fill the blowtorches ¾ full, turn them on and pump them so that they hum. Next, with a small flame, begin to heat the water and turn them off when it has low viscosity. Pump it some more and observe the blowtorches: if they go out, there is petrol in the heating vessel.
4. After half an hour, you can try the starter motor. If it does not start, keep heating some more.
5. When it finally runs, turn off the blowtorches and close the hatches!

1. Glysantin® (anti-freeze).

Footwear . . .

If you treat your footwear fickle,
You'll be in a bit of a pickle.
No hobnails on, all lacklustre,
You'll stand out at troop muster.
'Oh well, I'll be obstinate.'
It's as good as it will get:
In these jackboots, they're all shot,
Holes in socks, feet hurt a lot.
So with all 45 tonnes,
How do you think poor Panther runs?
Keep the running gear keep on running,
Keep your clean sheet already stunning:
Neglect will leave you on the field,
No driving on, your fate is sealed.

A cobbler is a worthy soul,
Who can your shoe resole.
And any Panther man, in fact,
Must know how to replace the tracks!

First, slacken and undo the tracks. Lay the tracks flat with the
bolt heads facing inwards. Drive or tow the Panther up to 1
metre in front of the end of the track (when marshaling this,
don't get lazy!). Attach the cable to the other end, over the idler
wheel and hanging over the sprocket. Keep the brake on the
other sprocket. Hoist up and fasten the track in one movement.

. . .Running gear

Break a . . .

A ski jump often can go wrong,
Make sure you don't fall headlong.
You'll break your bones, if you do
But no broken records too.
The Panther's axles are robust
On every bump they do adjust.
With the suspension torsion bar,
Can softly travel over terrain afar.
And so large, we know this thing,
Is the rotation of this spring.
**Don't scratch them with your tools,
They'll surely break on you fools!**
Shock absorbers do then block
From torsion bars the biggest shocks.
The same way the shoulder stops
The gun's recoil so you don't drop.

When driving, the shock absorbers should be already warmed up; if not, drive on a flat surface and top up with oil.
Should you need to **change** the **suspension arm**, jack it up high, hang a strap from it and tighten it onto the hull (tool 36). If there is an idler wheel underneath, lift the suspension arm again, hang the strap from it and then let it lower down. Release the domed cap nut and knock out the chock (leave the protective cover on). Unscrew the protective cover (tool 30) and pull out the suspension arm. Jack up the suspension arm with the shock absorber higher. On the shock absorber, remove the sheeting (only on the right) and at the fork end, undo the 2 screws (tool 17). Remove the bolts and unhook the shock absorbers. Undo the 2 nuts on the suspension arm and pull them out with the chock (box spanners 30 and 36).

What use is a Benz automobile
If on the journey it loses a wheel!
It's embarrassing and reprehensible,
The wheels are rather indispensable.
If you up to 60 endeavour,
You have got to put in the effort,
Changing a road wheel needs attention
With no tool misapprehension:
Road wheel, idler, hub, take care,
Else victory will be impaired.
Your Panther will on crutches go,
You're stupid if you don't see this so.

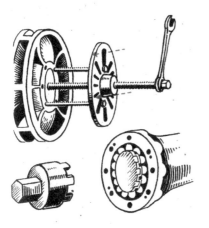

Changing a road wheel: Undo the 8 screws on the hub (tool 24), on the outer road wheels the (inner) nuts are on the rim. Then turn the wheel until the track teeth are at the top and the suspension arm is hanging from the hull. Now squeeze the road wheel on with two crowbars - make sure it is on the track correctly and don't you dare hurtle off if it isn't!

To take off the **hubs:** Undo the 4 countersunk screws to take off the hubcap. Undo the nut and twist it off. Take off the locking ring and the spacer ring and remove the hub from the suspension arm. When putting it back together: put the screws back on normally, then turn it a ¼ turn anti-clockwise to secure.

Changing an **idler wheel:** Undo the 6 screws (tool 22) and remove the cover. Under the big nut (tool 36), remove the washer and remove the wheel from the crank with the end plate.

If the straps aren't tightly clipped,
You can't get a decent grip.
Make long tracks smaller and tight,
The track bolts won't go quite right.
But if they are pulled too severe,
It'll ruin the running gear!
Hold the fourth wheel, so secure,
Then the track is on for sure.
If it's not right, adjust a bit,
With hex key 36 from your kit.

You must keep both slanting edges of the hex spindle horizontal so that the tension does not loosen and the protective cover closes properly. Smear some grease around the protective cover so it can seal better!

If the tracks are too long and you cannot tighten them any more, take track links out or change them. Knock in new bolts and secure them tightly!

Only open or close the track between the idler and the road wheel. Slacken the track and release it..

spannen

1

1. To tension.

Who did it?

A game of cards becomes uneasy
When the air makes you queasy.
After a while the delicate search
For the question does emerge:
What's the origin of this smell?
And why is it so bad as well?
The eating of all this army dough,
Constricts the gut, nowhere else to go.
Pressure and heat inflates, it's passed,
As we've said, an escape of gas.
If you do grind the clutch,
You'll soon realise as much,
That a noxious smell erupts
And fresh air it will corrupt...

...so keep your feet off the clutch!!

If you lose too much motion from the clutch, you must readjust it:

1. Take off the covering sheet behind the gearstick.
2. Step down on the clutch so that the clutch spring is released.
3. With an adjusting spanner, turn the nut with the hole in towards you, **1**, or down.
4. Clip all 3 locking washers, **2**, onto this nut and into the hole.
5. Release the clutch pedal.

Now measure between the nut and the withdrawal ring with the adjusting spanner, **3**!

Einstellmaß 20 mm[1]

1. Adjustment measurement 20 mm.

Steering of 4 . . .

Going four in hand is elegant,
You hold 4 HP in your hands.
With the Panther you'll soon wonder
At the horsepower of 700!
Four in hand, it's known therein,
In such a way, all harnessed in,
That all four horses see ahead,
And are all on the same stead.
If horses pull in other directions,
With steering there are imperfections.
So with seven hundred horses,
That can cause dangerous forces.
Panther runs in the way it picks,
If the steering is badly fixed.
Be mindful of adjustment measures,
Then your driving will be a pleasure!

and 700 horses

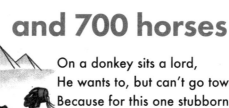

On a donkey sits a lord,
He wants to, but can't go towards.
Because for this one stubborn brute,
His steering is not resolute.
If you don't adjust the steering brake,
Your Panther'll be just as obstinate.

3 mm Spiel [1]

②

Therefore adjust:

...and don't forget the oil pressure pump! It
should never run dry!

What?	What is on it?	How?	What should it be?
Catch for the steering arm	Curved lever with a notch, **5**	Undo the 2 screws (tool 14). Move the curved lever so that the end of the steering lever is engaged in the middle.	When the engine is running, pull the steering lever up: when the clutch lever is up, the steering lever must be in the centre. But take care! The Panther will turn!
Clearance between roller lever, **1**, and cam face, **2**	Locking nut, **3** Adjusting nut, **4** Locking nut, **3**	Undo (tool 32) Turn until the clearance is correct, then tighten up	2-3 mm of clearance (mark this with an awl)
Release of the steering brake	Cam face, **2**	Undo the 2 screws (tool 14), then move over or under	Pull the steering brake 10 mm to the front of the centre point (mark this with an awl), the roller lever, **1**, must stand at the beginning of the curve. You will clearly feel how the roller tilts onto the rim of the cam face.

1. 3 mm of clearance.

When the brakes and the steering,
Are not in sync but interfering,
Does the momentum of the sleigh
On the first curve, it goes astray.
A crewman brakes to amend,
Instead of settling into the bend.
Be moderate, and just so,
Is how the Panther's steering goes.

Again – adjust:

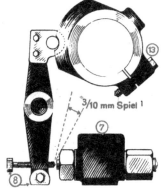

3/10 mm Spiel [1]

What?	What is on it?	How?	How should it be?
Clearance on the ball-shaped valve, **7**, on the steering clutch	Stop screw and locking screw, **8**	Pull the steering lever in to the centre, then adjust	Clearance between the stop screw and valve tappet is 3/10 of a mm (thickness of a clamping strip!)
Clearance on the steering clutch	6 screws Adjusting sleeve, **9**	Release (tool 17) With a hook wrench in the direction of travel. If it is too difficult, use a screw jack Tighten	When driving, put the clutch lever at the height of the red stripe on the housing cover, there should at least be a finger's width from the latch above
Overlay cam	6 screws Locking screw, **13**	Release (tool 17) Hit the cam upwards Hit the cam downwards Adjust when driving!	Overlay earlier Overlay later
Bite of the steering brake	Steering wheel (fine adjustment), **10**	If you turn right: brakes work too early If you turn left: brakes work too late	Put the steering level 10 mm over the centre, so that the steering brake bites. The steering lever must stay just as high when the brakes are applied!
Brake linkage	Steering wheel, **10** Connecting rod on the brake lever, **11** Steering wheel, **10**	Turn to the left Located in the deep hole Tighten	
Check the bite of the handbrake	Slide valve, **12** Brake housing	Remove Turn, and pull the handbrake	Brake housing should not be able to rotate both sides

1. 3/10 mm clearance.

Before starting . . .

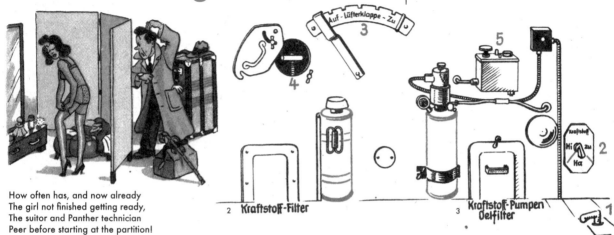

How often has, and now already
The girl not finished getting ready,
The suitor and Panther technician
Peer before starting at the partition!

2 Kraftstoff-Filter

3 Kraftstoff-Pumpen Oelfilter

Main battery switch	1	on	
Fuel tap	2	off	in the centre position 'main container'
Fan valve	3	closed	
Thermostat		closed	to the right of your sear
Gear		out	gear selector lever wiggles sideways here and there
Clearance-type filter		turn	more than once
Starter		on	pull the ring, then turn clockwise with 2 men so that the engine runs freely
		turn	(Water in exhaust?)
Crank, turn			
In the winter: strokes	5	fill	with 1 litre of petrol
10 plunges		pump	
Fans	4	off	pull the handle

1. Open-Airflow valve-Closed, 2. Fuel filter, 3. Fuel pumps oil filter.

Cranking up

If there's music to enjoy,
Dad takes trouble to employ
The crank, it is a tribulation,
Now just click it on, no frustration!
Today's life with the gramophone,
Makes, no doubt, a good tone!

Your notion that you can jump start the engine with two starters at the same time is a crackpot idea; if you do this, the starter will surely break!
Let the electrical starter motor run for 15 seconds at the most, then wait half a minute (in winter 2 minutes) and then once everything has come to a stop, you can try again.

Ignition key	in	position '0' ('1' Headlights, '2' Parking light)
Starter carburettor	pull	but don't press the accelerator
Clutch	step down	for the rigid transmission fluid acts as a brake
Starter motor	turn	until the engine starts up
Crank	out	
Accelerator pedal	touch lightly	until the little red light flickers
In the winter: pump 5	pump	until it is empty (slowly- the spark plugs will become wet)
Clutch starter carburettor	release	
	Gasgeben	but slowly apply some revs until the engine is up to 50°, then
Fan valve 3	open	
Thermostat	open	keep it in the centre if the water gets up to 70°
Brake	release	before you drive off.

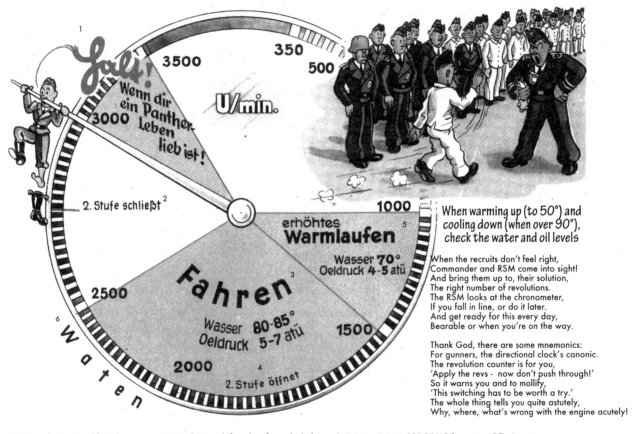

1. Stop! If a Panther life is dear to you!, 2. 2nd Stage (of cooling fan valve) closes, 3. Driving, Water 80°-85° Oil pressure 5-7 air pressure
Atü=Atmosphären Überdruck=Above atmospheric pressure, 4. 2nd Stage (of cooling fan valve) opens, 5. Increased warming up speed,
Water 70° Oil pressure 4-5 Above atmospheric pressure, 6. Wading.

Druckpunkt[1]

On flat ground, drive in 3rd gear and on climbs in 1st gear or 2nd gear. If you don't quite get into gear correctly, put the lever back into neutral, release the clutch and then press it down again - then it will work!

When the transmission oil is cold, gear changing does not work as smoothly; it is best to drive when it is warm! You will only change gear cleanly if you properly engage the clutch pedal to the floor and also bring the lever to its complete end position. You may also smoothly change gear by double-declutching but it is not necessary. **Don't yank and strangle it!!** Don't skip more than two gears when shifting downwards when the Panther has been driving for a while as it overloads the clutch.

If you don't hit the target's bullseye,
You haven't the right trigger pressure come by.
You'll find that you will miss a gear,
When you've not found the 'trigger pressure' here!
Changing gear with the pressure spot
Shows a key problem here a lot.
But theory doesn't hold much clout,
The main point really is **how!**
Changing up is more of a plight,
No revs, then trigger pressure, the bite;
Then push it gently into gear,
Without any clanking, awful to hear.
Take care at what is going on below,
The accelerator doesn't go,
Then without any noise or stress,
Briskly past the bite you do progress.
But at the dentist and you hear the crack,
You know well something's out of whack.
'Stop!' shouts severely the gearbox,
Please treat me like I'm Goldilocks!

The index finger, with the crook of the first finger or with the middle finger, gauges the feeling on the trigger and presses it by bending in such a way until the resistance is felt; this means that you have reached the 'trigger pressure'. Then immediately bend the finger again.
Army Publication 240, Item 73, Paragraph 2

1. Trigger pressure.

Changing gear

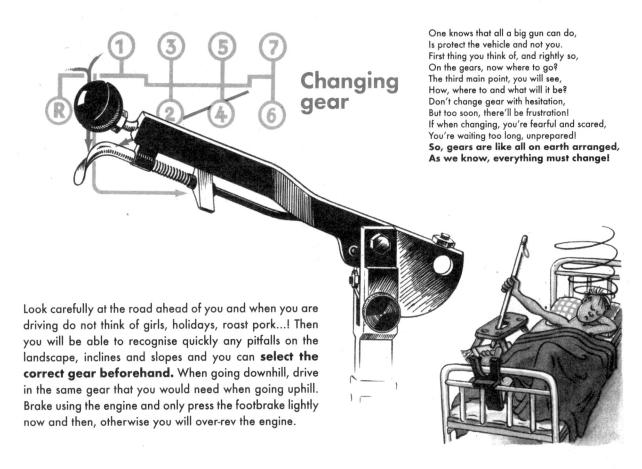

One knows that all a big gun can do,
Is protect the vehicle and not you.
First thing you think of, and rightly so,
On the gears, now where to go?
The third main point, you will see,
How, where to and what will it be?
Don't change gear with hesitation,
But too soon, there'll be frustration!
If when changing, you're fearful and scared,
You're waiting too long, unprepared!
**So, gears are like all on earth arranged,
As we know, everything must change!**

Look carefully at the road ahead of you and when you are driving do not think of girls, holidays, roast pork...! Then you will be able to recognise quickly any pitfalls on the landscape, inclines and slopes and you can **select the correct gear beforehand.** When going downhill, drive in the same gear that you would need when going uphill. Brake using the engine and only press the footbrake lightly now and then, otherwise you will over-rev the engine.

Pale and world-weary thus,
Sat Paul once on the bus.
Driver notices, the vehicle's bumping,
Paul's dinner's come back up pumping.
Society'll his manners criticise,
But they cost a fee in size!
On a journey you don't feel well,
Consequence, to breakfast bid farewell.
And accelerate with feet of lead,
So breakfast's in a bucket instead!

Gas geben [1]

The superior driver steals courage from their opponent and heart from their audience - this is what you need to understand: drive like you've won!

Nietzsche

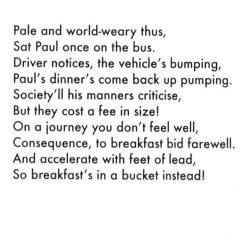

With revs and with gears you will find,
You must keep Caracciola in mind.
He never drives faster than he must,
The fastest is mostly just:
Who leads for a long time from the start,
Is later the one who's not so smart.
So when in an action-packed race,
He has to preserve his calm and pace.
His secret is hypothetically,
Open the throttle with care, then energetically!
You won't always win a medal,
But the accelerator is the pedal.
The thing is small, what a shame,
But in the Panther it's the name of the game!
Only under weak and dim lights,
You find accelerator pedal in fright;
The situation can be a bit hairy,
Many fail this, be wary.
Representatives from the other side,
Are not always the cleverest implied.
Whoever then stubbornly hoofs it,
Is with the engine, not a good fit!

1. Opening the throttle.

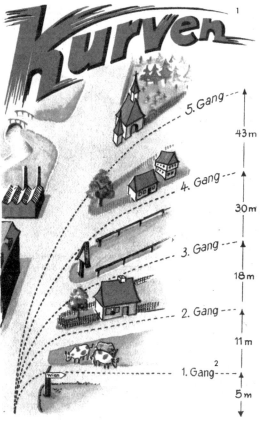

Kurven

You can make small adjustments to your direction by lightly pulling the steering lever, accelerating or knocking the revs back. Pull through until it hits the notch to travel around the bend; but you must be in the right gear. Turning in a position out of gear is very good, but you need a lot of space. Instead, make sure you are in gear so you don't ram your comrades or their vehicles.

Scrape through difficult terrain using the steering brake, turn the hand wheel on the right of the steering lever to the right; by doing this your suspension will re-tense. If the oil pressure system fails, you must then turn the steering wheel hard to the left.

Brake only with the footbrake or the handbrake, because if you yank both steering levers, the steering brake drum will fly apart or break the shaft.

Drive only with the gun in the 12 o'clock position, but don't tickle the man in front with the barrel!

5. Gang

43 m

4. Gang

30 m

3. Gang

18 m

2. Gang

11 m

1. Gang

5 m

Flying quickly, wondrous and well,
It is called a carousel.
Beginning slowly you do **swerve**,
Only in a small **curve.**
With a much larger speed,
This curve gets bigger indeed.
And when you do contemplate,
It does with steering correlate.
You do drive hell for leather,
A larger arc is put together.
And flatter curve, but then mark:
Sharp curve but tighter **arc.**
On the other hand, drive too gentle,
To do this is not instrumental.
The steering brake will come a cropper.
If you think it's right and proper;
Whoever the transmission wrecks
Will become a carriage driver next!

1. Turning radius, 2. Gear.

In winter there is frost and ice,
Looking back it was quite nice.
Children leg it and couples step out
Not alone in enjoyment, no doubt.
No, there's a chap of advancing years
Sliding on the ice with cheer.
On such a length of good trackway,
Rules and laws do go astray.
A postlady does slip over cursorily,
Her dress slides up quite immorally.
In short, all that's worthy and dignified
Is bold and merry when you can slide.
But some 'events' can be quite drastic,
It goes wrong, you're not made of elastic.
You'll often slide when you don't want to there,
So when it's slippery, travel with care...
and

Eis und Glätte [1]

Pull the steering lever gently. Go without the brakes and on a downward gradient take off the revs, countersteer and let the Panther slide. If it slides wildly on flat terrain, put your foot down and it will right itself.

Ice of a thickness of ¾ metre over water can carry the Panther if it is consistently light and clear. Be careful on river banks, directly over currents and snow-covered ice because it will be thinner. Look carefully at the route you will take over the river. If it doesn't look safe, wait or leave it well alone.

When crossing: Open your hatches! Do not stop, turn or change gear; instead **cross smoothly on your own.** If the ice begins to sag, speed up gently, otherwise you will go through the ice.

1. Ice and slipperiness.

88

KNÜPPELDÄMMLICHES [1]

For wheels is the causeway produced,
It'll tear a strip off you in use.
Tracks have a broad expanse,
But why is this in circumstance?
Well, away from the bridge,
You can drive through the squidge -

- if you drive quickly through it without changing gear or making
any sharp turns. But too much acceleration is just as bad as too
little (stalled engine) - **give your tracks time to grip!**

Panthers, the pious chorus prefer:
'Protect us, O, Saint Christopher.
Bless us and all of our deeds,
Especially when wading like you indeed!'

In the east, you can drive through rivers as they are wide but
shallow; you can't always rely on there being a tank bridge.
Block the holes between the engine and the fan compartments
with wooden pegs, so the Panther can go up to 1½ metres
in water! It is essential that you **set sail in 1st or 2nd gear**
(bow wave!) and do not stop. Keep the gun high!

The river bed should not be muddy; if the banks are not firm and
flat, the engineer troops can help. If more want to cross, go one
after each other, then nothing should happen.

And - whoever tries it once, doesn't like wading!

1. Ein Knüppeldamm is a log road. Knüppeldämmliches is a play on words. Dämlich means stupid = 'log road stupidity'.

Ritterminen[1]

The castle walls make the knights,
Go through bars, bridges, mud from a height.
Today the means are technically advanced,
But in cruel effect much more enhanced!
Once from the walls poured the pitch,
Now mines crouch down in a ditch.
And so with a sharp eye steadfast,
Can upon these mines do cast.
But out the Panther you can't see well,
Or see what's there - a death knell.
In dangerous areas on the hunt,
Follow the one who's out in front.
In a minefield it's advised,
That you stop, immobilised...

...and reverse in your own tracks. Don't stay still out of fear as you'll be a target. On suspicious terrain, keep your eyes open! Peculiar molehills, conspicuous cracks (particularly after rain), withered grass, discoloured ground or dirty snow are dangerous. Enemy mines are often laid out in a grid pattern. In any event, keep away from the mines and mark out the field with branches. If you don't have the correct capabilities, then leave the mines as they are, but it is best to deactivate them by blowing them up. With small obstructions you can solve them on your own but for larger ones, you will need the engineer troops. When they do help you, don't just sit and watch: help them by being able to give covering fire!

The most important thing: report it!

1. Knight's mines.

Sperren[1]

If you joyous and light-hearted,
From the Front on holiday departed,
If have holiday on a Sunday,
But your suit's in disarray,
If in the pub at night,
With scrumptious meal in delight,
If cheerfully have a look around,
But your lady has something found:
Everywhere - when she takes hold of you,
Waits an army patrol with things to do,
They do make a stand against,
Unkindly is your progress tense.
Try to avoid where they're located,
Striving to be evaded.
Finally, you are then caught;
Your ploy didn't work as it ought.

So gentlemen, take instruction,
Malicious are these obstructions!
Look around you precisely
That your avoidance does work nicely.
Drive over a mine, a convergence,
It's much worse than a divergence!

By fixed street obstacles, you must also expect mines and hidden extras, so 'examine' it first with a high explosive shell or divert around it in a wide arc! Anti-tank ditches with shallow banks can be crossed but V-shaped ditches are very dangerous! You will never get out of them on your own! It's the same with deep ruts in hilly terrain; here the engineer troops will use a slanted ramp to get you out. Don't drive beaming with joy over anti-tank ditches as they are definitely mined!

1. Obstacles.

A man drives a Mercedes-Benz,
But to plumpness he himself lends.
He loves the hills and goes walking,
As up there no sins are stalking.
He steps on a bridge so weak,
Quite confident of his physique.
As a consequence of his weight,
It breaks, the wood has a change of state!
He falls off and so it seems,
Underneath, gets wet from the stream.
Joe on the bank, laughing overjoyed,
His sides are splitting with Schadenfreud'.
And so he takes it on the chin,
That Alpine pastures aren't free from sin.

1

For you it's like going over this creek,
Bridges are often much too weak.
Look first at its condition,
Before you cross it on a mission.
If made out of walls or concrete,
They'll carry your Panther complete.
Wooden bridges are often frail,
Such bridges are just prone to fail...but,

If you are away from the combat zone in a busy area and it was built by Organisation Todt or the bridging engineer battalions (24 t), you can attempt to cross. Iron bridges (24 t) of the new variant can also carry the Panther, but with older and weaker bridges, first use the engineers. Never exceed the stated weight capacity of a military bridge (or any military bridge system or any military wooden temporary bridge)!

Take care, as the carriageway on reinforced concrete bridges is very weak! Look out for cracks or fissures while crossing and the engineers should lay down a strong wooden surface.

It is no longer advised that one Panther at a time should cross the bridge; this is so the whole detachment can cross it. When proceeding over a precarious bridge, the supports and columns must be constantly observed for any damage.

Stop just before the bridge and let yourself be directed onto it, so you don't need to steer, change gear, accelerate, brake or stop while on the bridge! Drive smoothly in 4th gear and only crank it back up when you are far enough away from the bridge. Otherwise the bridge might collapse from your shenanigans. On good quality bridges, drive at a distance of 30 metres, but if you have doubts, cross one at a time.

1. Bridges.

Recovery

The winner is he who's strong,
Because he pulls the others along.
In sport well-loved is this game,
And by Panthers it is the same.
And it gives some pleasure now,
To then briskly draw the plough.
The 18-tonner it must toil,
To pull the Panther out the soil.
Which, you spot with consternation,
From enemies no underestimation.
If Panther's stuck in the muck,
It won't move from that spot, stuck.

Pull with machines 2, then 1 man leads the whole thing through!

First:
Where I'm sat, I **let** my senior **know,**
Exactly the **location** do I show.
The Panther, what is its state,
And if my **steering** operates.
If it's with or without **tracks,**
If it's easy or hard to get back.

Then:
Lay your **ropes** down flat prior,
Else they'll tear off the strongest wire.
A rope will fly up in your face,
If a **sharp edge** bends in place.
Keep away your head and hands,
They won't kinks and **knots** withstand.

When being towed forwards, lash the turret down at the 6 o'clock direction, if backwards, at 12 o'clock. Keep in communication with your comrades in the recovery vehicle, then it will all proceed quickly!

Crewmen in the recovery troop! You cannot bring enough crowbars, S-hooks, shackles, track pins, ropes, plans and tools along when you set out!!

PANTHER-KLINIK [1]

The workshop's not just for a doze,
They can't do everything there, you know.
But look, you must get involved,
Above all tell what needs to be solved.
To the **Foreman** you must say,
What is wrong with the vehicle today;
The **Armourer** then will be told,
What with the gun is to behold;
Signals men will want to find out,
Whether the radio system's in doubt.
Announce without being indirect,
Very clearly what has been wrecked.
Remove ammunition at the outset,
Before you in **workshops** do get!

Then take out all of your bags,
Leaving them, they're as good as rags.
So if a part has been defaced,
It must then be replaced.
Don't throw it to the side of the road,
To the inspector it must be showed;
Bring him what has fallen apart,
He'll get you a brand new part.
But don't push for additions,
And stay by your tank in position.
Because even sometimes the specialist,
Forgets essentials, they can be missed.
And often after a time finite,
Your Panther's ready again to fight!

1. Panther Clinic.

Parking up

Once in the grey times of antiquity,
A man afforded some ubiquity.
He himself around for hours hauled,
And at the end two words called,
With a last bit of energy he finished,
Fell on the marketplace, diminished.
Of his run is now a story told,
There are medals made of gold;
But now a runner can attain,
To do this without being slain.
Because at the finish there's a snack,
And then he gets a warm compress pack.
When he gets cold because he sweats,
The engine's strongly with heat beset:
So, park up, and take a breather,
Rest before running any further!

Russia's famously large surroundings,
Make possibilities so astounding.
As far as they can, in these regions,
Panthers spread out their legions.
Note serious warnings, by and large,
Think of wind shelter, cover, camouflage!

Hand brake	pull,	
Ignition key (also the parking light)	off	in position '0'
In the winter: start-up process	pull	softening the film of oil
Gearing	push in	
Edge filter	turn	more than once
Ventilation flap, fuel tap	on	
Battery master switch	off	

Do not forget in winter to thin the oil and lay brushwood, planks or straw underneath the tracks.
Sweep snow from the Panther and cover the air intake grate.

Firstly, you must travel . . .

There's no way you can argue
That in peacetime, Germany hadn't through
Motorsport proven it's worth
In all four corners of the earth.
For many it was a long expedition,
To get our cars to the starting position.
Likewise, the Panther tank crews
The railways, they do reuse.
All loaded up, better in traction,
They get you in place ready for action.

When loading:

Get yourself in front of the loading ramp in such a way that you do not need to steer to get into the middle of the trailer. Only put your Panther on transport vehicles that can hold over 50 tonnes, as standard transport vehicles can only hold up to 35 tonnes. Load on via the ramp and use the whole length of the vehicle, not driving on at an angle. Otherwise you won't fit or the tracks will jam and the Panther will slip off.

Loading up is like making a good sauce. Both have to work at the first attempt and you can't make them better afterwards. Otherwise, you have to start again from scratch.
Balzac

Stay steady: in summer, tighten the handbrake, in winter, put it in 1st gear and close all hatch covers.

Take off the side skirts and store them underneath the Panther. Lash the turret down in the 12 o'clock direction.

Nail on 2 wooden wedges at the front and back of the tracks (if you don't have these, use beams and a large wedge on the idler wheels). Slide on and secure the vehicle's loading sleepers to the tracks.

During the journey. . . . . . . check regularly that:

the **brakes** are engaged,
the **tracks** and the **loading sleepers** are secure, particularly when ice and snow is thawing, the Panther stays in the **centre of the wagon;** you can look things up in the loading manual in the vehicle.

En route and on bridge crossings there is a higher chance of danger! Because of this, do not stand or lie on the Panther during the journey!

'First win - then travel' they do say,
Railway boss Dorpmüller knows the way!
But you load the Panther not for fun,
It's the other way round, 'First travel - then win!'
You need lots of locos and wagons in the war,
For victory they do roll for.
But what use are wagons, in decision,
If they fail to deliver provisions!

.:... **dann siegen !** [1]

1... then win!

Epilog an Dich im Himmel[1]

Five, in time consecrated,
They in heaven are awaited.
Each one thought what they are worth;
What they did wrong when on earth.
But in this heavenly domain,
To atone it's too late, all in vain.
To those five it is unknown,
What was in Panther Primer shown.
Ignorance is detrimental,
In this case, fatally monumental.
So you see, it would have been better,
If in the book they'd read each letter.
Too late now in paradise,
But you've got time to learn it twice.

Now, comrades, listen in, on guard,
What you need to learn is not that hard.
You will learn with cheery pluck,
But if you're forced, you'll come unstuck.
Take the Panther Primer in hand.
You know that under humour stands,
The serious nature of the war,
Of which the Primer forces you more,
To make you into a Panther crewman,
That means an outstanding human.
But the soldier does his duty
Never with a face stubborn and snooty.
What you must know, learn it steadily,
Learn it well yourself, and do it readily!

1. Epilogue to you in heaven, 2. St Hubert Please knock, 3. St Barbara Registration on Cloud 9.

98

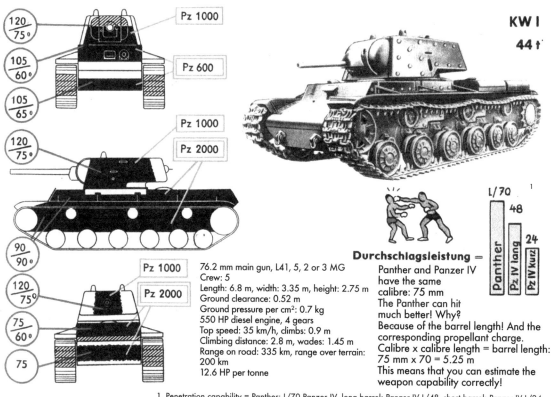

KW I

44 t

120 / 75° → Pz 1000

105 / 60° → Pz 600

105 / 65°

Pz 1000

Pz 2000

120 / 75°

90 / 90°

120 / 75°

75 / 60°

75

Pz 1000

Pz 2000

76.2 mm main gun, L41, 5, 2 or 3 MG
Crew: 5
Length: 6.8 m, width: 3.35 m, height: 2.75 m
Ground clearance: 0.52 m
Ground pressure per cm²: 0.7 kg
550 HP diesel engine, 4 gears
Top speed: 35 km/h, climbs: 0.9 m
Climbing distance: 2.8 m, wades: 1.45 m
Range on road: 335 km, range over terrain: 200 km
12.6 HP per tonne

L/70

48

24

Panther | Pz IV lang | Pz IV kurz

Durchschlagsleistung =
Panther and Panzer IV
have the same
calibre: 75 mm
The Panther can hit
much better! Why?
Because of the barrel length! And the
corresponding propellant charge.
Calibre x calibre length = barrel length:
75 mm x 70 = 5.25 m
This means that you can estimate the
weapon capability correctly!

1. Penetration capability = Panther: L/70 Panzer IV, long barrel: Panzer IV L/48, short barrel: Panzer IV L/24.

T 34   8 43

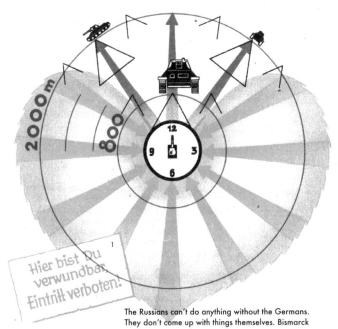

2000m

800

12
9   3
6

Soviet tanks, as you've viewed,
Unsubstantial is their food.
But it seems the way it goes,
They have a gut full of potatoes.
These tanks, from afar, on the hop,
Have a pointy head up top.
The T 34 is the first profile,
It is sleek and full of guile.
Its big belly is so large;
So bounce off will most shots discharged.
Hit the pointy turret, that's what to do,
Especially if at an angle, askew.
From the side and back, do begin,
As much as you can, shots do go in.
The profile here, you can see,
T 34: 8–4–3.

Hier bist Du
verwundbar
Eintritt verboten! [1]

The Russians can't do anything without the Germans.
They don't come up with things themselves. Bismarck

1. Here you are vulnerable, No entry!

KW I 6 64

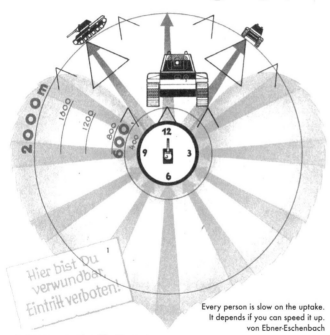

2000m
1600
1200
800
600
400

12
9 ☐ 3
6

Hier bist Du
verwundbar,
Eintritt verboten![1]

Every person is slow on the uptake.
It depends if you can speed it up.
von Ebner-Eschenbach

1. Here you are vulnerable, No entry!

The next tank type up to tricks,
Is the typical Bolshevik.
It's not so visible from outside,
That it's heavily fortified.
A pointy turret and full of potatoes;
As this tank also shows.
From the front hit the Soviet,
Fire well onto the turret.
The back and the side, however,
Built for heavy shots was it never.
Because all tanks, protection's sparse,
Are weak on the kidneys and the arse.
You know that all your strength lies,
In the slogan: stubborness is wise.
With the KV-1, don't ignore
the profile, always: 6 – 6 – 4.

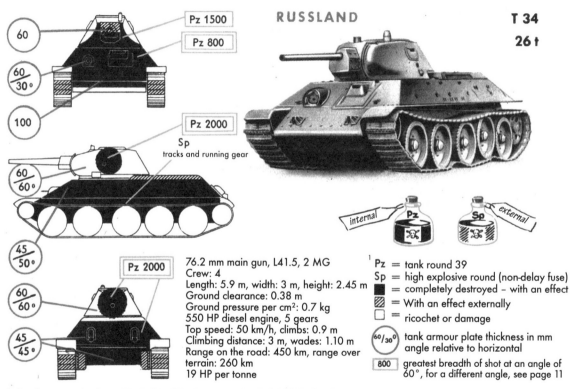

RUSSLAND

T 34

26 t

60

Pz 1500

Pz 800

60 / 30°

100

Pz 2000

Sp
tracks and running gear

60 / 60°

45 / 50°

Pz 2000

60 / 60°

45 / 45°

internal   Pz   Sp   external

76.2 mm main gun, L41.5, 2 MG
Crew: 4
Length: 5.9 m, width: 3 m, height: 2.45 m
Ground clearance: 0.38 m
Ground pressure per cm²: 0.7 kg
550 HP diesel engine, 5 gears
Top speed: 50 km/h, climbs: 0.9 m
Climbing distance: 3 m, wades: 1.10 m
Range on the road: 450 km, range over
terrain: 260 km
19 HP per tonne

[1] Pz = tank round 39
Sp = high explosive round (non-delay fuse)
■ = completely destroyed – with an effect
▨ = With an effect externally
☐ = ricochet or damage

60/30° tank armour plate thickness in mm
angle relative to horizontal

800 greatest breadth of shot at an angle of
60°, for a different angle, see page 11

1. Pz = Panzergranate = Armour Piercing Round Sp = Sprenggranate = High Explosive Round.

SU 122

Alte Bekannte[1]

The same tanks are useful, no buts
They are used like a Sturmgeschütz.
With fear you will these words atone,
When suddenly they are nearer shown.
Your gun will, in some detail,
Take the wind out of their sails.
Secondly, the gun's concerned,
With hitting your side and the stern.
But this is the well-known joke,
The front by assault gun, won't be broke!
The following do keep in your aim:
Length, width, strength are the same.
Looking through the glass in location,
Can use the same target calibration.

122 mm assault gun, SU-122, 30 tonnes
122 m howitzer, L22.7 and MG
45 separate cartridge ammunition
Field of fire: height + 25° – 2°, side: per 10°
Total elevation: 2.15 m, elevation of fire: 1.35 m
All round armour: 45 mm, crew: 4–5

85 mm assault gun, SU-85, 30 tonnes
85 mm tank gun, L51.5 and MG
48 separate cartridge ammunition
Elevation: height + 15° – 6°, side: per 10°
Total elevation: 2.36 m, elevation of fire:1.50 m
All round armour 45 mm, crew: 4–5

SU 85

1. Old friends.

Das Stachelmaß[1]

The wanton maid does arise,
Upon the first attack from the skies.
But the girl's stand-offish in mind,
You must get a bit closer inclined.
So with the Panther it's the same,
As with a girl, the fighting game.

You're a Panther man, you're a best friend,
When in range, can apprehend!
The specialist does this, so theoretical,
Quite easy: using the pointed reticle!

At the back and the side too,
2000 m they fall victim to you.
But out front important is the spike,
It tells you if you'll make the strike!
That is to say, the range of the shell,
Even for you it will serve well.

You must for larger armour strength,
Look at the profiles all in length.
A number will say to you and then:
'Whether you can hit it and when!'
Look here, how easy this can be:
T-34: **8 – 4 – 3.**
The **8** will show you at the start
How near or how far you can be apart.

800 metres, keep up your chin!
For shooting he's ready to begin!

The point you need in front is 4,
This number, we'll impart once more,
A shot at the right time supplied,
If out front is 4 lines wide.
So you have, in this instance,
It fits between 2 spikes in distance.

The last number we have here is 3,
How the reticle from the side will be.
To be shown to you from the side,
It only needs to be 3 lines wide.
So it's at **2000** in position,
And onto the side goes ammunition.

When from the back you evaluate,
The number's only half as great.
That is (as clear as in front of your face),
1 and a ½, in this case.

In glass so wide does the rear appear,
As it's just **2000** near.
As he is, stay fixed on the spot,
Happy hunting, now away with the shot!

T 34:

8 = 4 = 3

800 m   4 Strich[2]   3 Strich

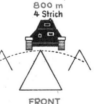

800 m
4 Strich

FRONT

2000 m
3 Strich

SEITE

2000 m
1½ Strich

HECK

1. Measuring on the pointed reticle, 2. Strich = Line = MOA = Minute of Angle.

in neuem Gewande

The gun itself is very strong,
To underestimate it would be wrong.
For every assault gun kind,
Think of Siegfried's weak behind.
Don't be appalled, don't be surprised,
When you look at the calibre size.
Alone gunpowder doesn't suffice,
The calibre length is more precise,
The T-34 and KV-1
Some things they do, some others none.
They can in the area wobble about,
Like Sturmgeschütz they do act out,
And then are turret without,
Like a 'storm' they do break out.

SU 152

KW 85

152 mm assault gun, SU-152, 50 tonnes
152 mm howitzer, L29 and sub-MG
20 separate cartridge ammunition
Elevation: height + 20° – 3.5°, side: per 12°
Total elevation: 2.5 m, elevation of fire: 1.8 m
60 mm armour all round, 5 man crew

KV-85 tank, 46 tonnes
85 mm tank gun, L51.5 and 3 MG
71 separate fixed ammunition
Elevation: height + 23° – 4°, side: 360°
Total elevation: 2.9 m, elevation of fire: 2 m
60–75 mm armour all round
Turret: 110 mm cast steel, 5 man crew

1. In new clothes.

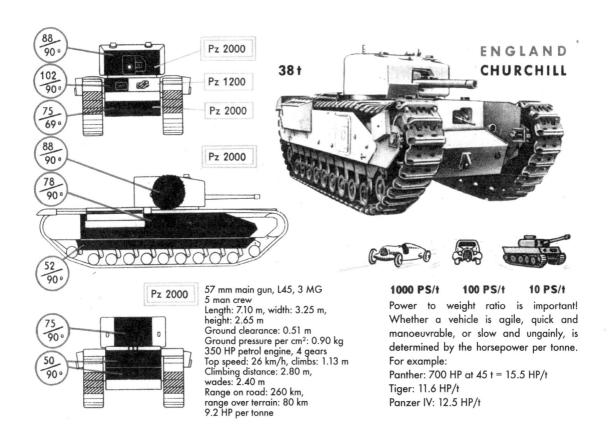

88/90°
102/90°
75/69°
88/90°
78/90°
52/90°
75/90°
50/90°

Pz 2000
Pz 1200
Pz 2000
Pz 2000
Pz 2000

38 t

ENGLAND
CHURCHILL

57 mm main gun, L45, 3 MG
5 man crew
Length: 7.10 m, width: 3.25 m,
height: 2.65 m
Ground clearance: 0.51 m
Ground pressure per cm²: 0.90 kg
350 HP petrol engine, 4 gears
Top speed: 26 km/h, climbs: 1.13 m
Climbing distance: 2.80 m,
wades: 2.40 m
Range on road: 260 km,
range over terrain: 80 km
9.2 HP per tonne

1000 PS/t   100 PS/t   10 PS/t

Power to weight ratio is important!
Whether a vehicle is agile, quick and
manoeuvrable, or slow and ungainly, is
determined by the horsepower per tonne.
For example:
Panther: 700 HP at 45 t = 15.5 HP/t
Tiger: 11.6 HP/t
Panzer IV: 12.5 HP/t

Sherman 10 33

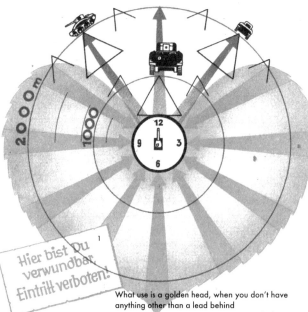

What use is a golden head, when you don't have anything other than a lead behind

Luther

1. Here you are vulnerable, No entry!.

Best quality clothes from a good retailer,
Are made to measure by a tailor.
But Uncle Sam's clothing's ready-made
From a large shop in the trade.
From one cast, head to toe,
But here and there's a hole to show.
From head to toe this tank does wear,
A skirt from armour-plate casting there.
It looks as if it's a perfect fit,
But fired at it will easily split.
On the flanks and on its rump,
Fire down low to give him a bump.
It's head is tough, but happy hunting,
On superstructure when confronting.
For Shermans, when on shooting spree,
On the profile it's: 10 – 3 – 3.

Churchill 20 24

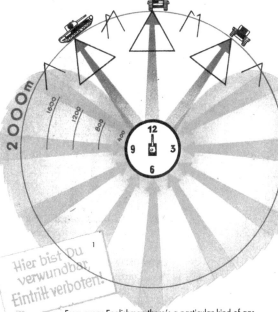

2000m 1600 1200 800 400

12
9 3
6

The Tommy's housewife's cooking's rotten
So food outside the house is gotten.
Cameroon, Togo, the colonies,
Are the British fayre, yes please.
For water he doesn't think critically,
It's British if it tastes of the sea.
A tank's stomach of some weight,
Can most hard hits tolerate.
But Churchill's lofty brow within,
There does lie a squishy noggin.
If you can get it just right,
It's expected, can give it a fright.
From the side and back, this old ruse,
Can fire deep in to cause a bruise.
For Churchill, look at it once more:
On the profile: 20 – 2 and 4.

Hier bist Du verwundbar. Eintritt verboten! 1

From every Englishman there's a particular kind of gas
emitted; a lethal stuffy air of tediousness.   Heinrich Heine

1. Here you are vulnerable, No entry!

85/55⁰ → Pz 1200

56/30⁰ → Pz 1000

56 → Pz 2000

85/90⁰ → Pz 2000

Pak 7,62
L/52,8; 1 MG

M 10 auf Sherman-
Fahrgestell
30 t

1

39/90⁰ → Pz 2000

85/90⁰

26/90⁰

60/82⁰

SHERMAN
← **29 t**

75 mm main gun, L40, 3 MG
5 man crew
Length: 6.10 m, width: 2.9 m, height: 2.8 m
Ground clearance: 0.4 m
Ground pressure per cm^2: 1.29 kg
400 HP petrol engine, 5 gears
Top speed: 40 km/h, climbs: 0.9 m
Climbing distance: 2.45 m, wading: 0.9 m
Range on roads: 300 km,
range over terrain: 180 km
13.3 HP per tonne

80%

100%

To pour or to roll, that is the
question! You can indeed pour the
whole external surface more quickly and more tidily in one piece
(Sherman) than cut out the plate,
weld and seal the drilled holes (us).
For the same thickness, however,
you can crack it at 500 m earlier.
Rolled steel is the best!

1. 76.2 mm anti-tank gun L52.8 and 1 MG, M10 on Sherman chassis 30 t.

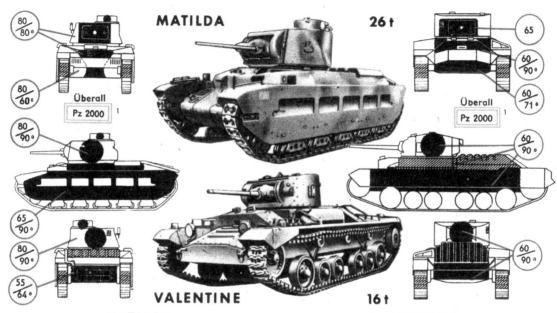

MATILDA

26 t

80/80°

80/60°

Überall

Pz 2000 [1]

65

60/90°

60/71°

Überall

Pz 2000 [1]

80/90°

65/90°

80/90°

55/64°

60/90°

60/90°

VALENTINE

16 t

M A T I L D A

76.2 mm main gun, L26.5, 1 MG
4 man crew
Length: 6 m, width: 2.55 m, height: 2.5 m
Ground clearance: 0.33 m
Ground pressure per cm²: 1.14 kg

2 x 100 HP diesel engines, 6 gears
Top speed: 23 km/h, climbs: 0.6 m
Climbing distance: 1.8 m, wading: 0.8 m
Range on road: 100 km, range over
terrain: 60 km
7.8 HP per tonne

V A L E N T I N E

40 mm main gun, L52, 1 MG
3 man crew
Length: 5.45 m, width: 2.75 m,
height: 2.25 m
Ground clearance: 0.42 m
Ground pressure per cm²: 0.72 kg

130 HP diesel engine, 5 gears
Top speed: 30 km/h, climbs: 0.7 m
Climbing distance: 2.40 m, wading: 1.20 m
Range on road: 150 km,
range over terrain: 100 km
8.1 HP per tonne

1. Everywhere.

Lee 20 13

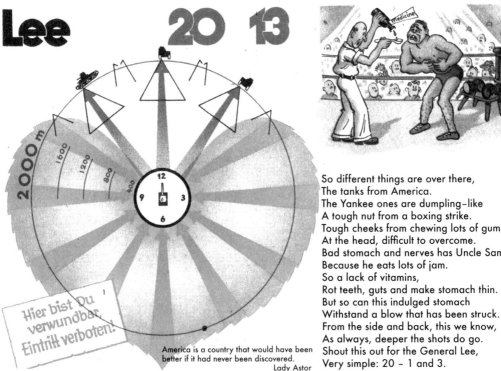

2 0 0 0 m

1600 1200 800 400

12
9 3
6

Medicine

Hier bist Du verwundbar,
Eintritt verboten![1]

America is a country that would have been
better if it had never been discovered.
Lady Astor

So different things are over there,
The tanks from America.
The Yankee ones are dumpling–like
A tough nut from a boxing strike.
Tough cheeks from chewing lots of gum,
At the head, difficult to overcome.
Bad stomach and nerves has Uncle Sam,
Because he eats lots of jam.
So a lack of vitamins,
Rot teeth, guts and make stomach thin.
But so can this indulged stomach
Withstand a blow that has been struck.
From the side and back, this we know,
As always, deeper the shots do go.
Shout this out for the General Lee,
Very simple: 20 – 1 and 3.

1. Here you are vulnerable, No entry!.

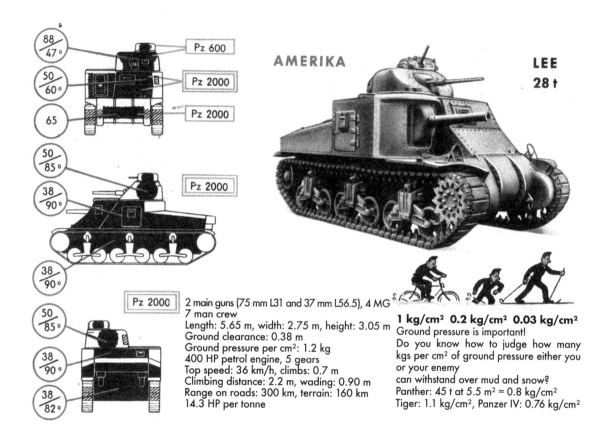

AMERIKA

LEE
28 t

88/47°
Pz 600

50/60°
Pz 2000

65
Pz 2000

50/85°

38/90°
Pz 2000

38/90°

50/85°

38/90°

38/82°

Pz 2000

2 main guns (75 mm L31 and 37 mm L56.5), 4 MG
7 man crew
Length: 5.65 m, width: 2.75 m, height: 3.05 m
Ground clearance: 0.38 m
Ground pressure per cm²: 1.2 kg
400 HP petrol engine, 5 gears
Top speed: 36 km/h, climbs: 0.7 m
Climbing distance: 2.2 m, wading: 0.90 m
Range on roads: 300 km, terrain: 160 km
14.3 HP per tonne

1 kg/cm² 0.2 kg/cm² 0.03 kg/cm²
Ground pressure is important!
Do you know how to judge how many
kgs per cm² of ground pressure either you
or your enemy
can withstand over mud and snow?
Panther: 45 t at 5.5 m² = 0.8 kg/cm²
Tiger: 1.1 kg/cm², Panzer IV: 0.76 kg/cm²

Matilda und Valentine

20 13

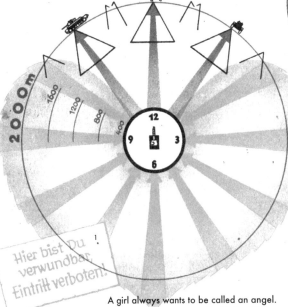

2000m
1600
1200
800
400

12
9 3
6

Hier bist Du verwundbar
Eintritt verboten! [1]

A girl always wants to be called an angel.
It is a given.   Karl Julius Weber

As a specialist you know the sign,
Of Matilda and of Valentine.
Beforehand they were a taboo,
Now they fall in a heartbeat too.
The profile: 20 – 1 and 3
Look, the two are light and easy.
Through the 1, clearly is assigned,
Both of them do walk the line.
From a thread hangs the reputation
Of such girls from this location.
It is much the same case,
With the light tanks in place.
Light, easy ones you can forfeit,
As long as they don't see you do it.
Make a note of 20 – 1 and 3,
It'll come off, go for it, see.

1. Here you are vulnerable, No entry!.